AN EXTRACT FROM *MAKING FILMS FOR PLEASURE AND PROFIT*
BY LORD BADEN-POWELL

ON FINDING A DIRECTOR...
Finding a director is no granny knot. Directors are nearly as important as
Scoutmasters - so the Sunday papers tell us. After taking your cold shower,
learn to spot a director. This is easily done as they all wear jodhpurs and have
their hats on back to front. To find a director, simply follow the tracks of his
broken marriages. If you think you can do it by yourself, take another cold
shower and think again.

Which is precisely what Tim, Bill and Graeme did ... and just look at the
results!

CONTENTS
IN ALPHABETICAL ORDER

First published in Great Britain by Weidenfeld & Nicolson Ltd. 1977

Copyright © Tim Brooke-Taylor, Graeme Garden and Bill Oddie, 1977

First Sphere Books edition 1978

Designed by Anthony Cohen

Printed in Great Britain by Severn Valley Press Ltd.

TRADE
MARK

CHAPTER ONE

Ivan looked at his watch. Ten minutes late he thought. He searched the sky, but there was still no sign of the Piper Apache that 'Marshmallow' had promised him. The East German forest had been silent, only the sound of his breathing as he had laid out the landing markers had given sign of any life at all. But now he could hear the dogs. He felt no animosity towards these creatures, they were just an instrument of their masters, no more a willing partner than a rifle or a stick of gelignite. Yet, as Ivan knew only too well, they could be just as dangerous. As he moved towards the controls of the Combine Harvester he remembered Gretchen. Was it only last night as they lay huddled in each other's arms, he had promised he would never leave her? She had laughed when he said only a fool would leave a girl who made the best Bortsch in the world. She had gone to sleep smiling and she would still be smiling when the early shift found her on Monday morning. Poor Gretchen she had trusted him, but surely better his way than theirs.

The Combine Harvester roared into life. He let out the clutch and the huge machine rumbled slowly forward. 'Only a fool' thought Ivan as he jumped to the ground. 'Only a fool' he whispered as the revolving blades moved inexorably towards him.
'Only a fool. Only a fool. Only a fool.' The machinery seemed to take up his lament. He glanced for the last time at his watch . . . 9.29.

And then the blades were upon him.

At exactly the same moment, in England, three brave men were about to make a decision which was to change the course of history. This might just have been co-incidence; but ten years later, only sixty miles away in Northampton, a man was fixing the exhaust on his car, completely unaware of what was about to happen on the following Thursday. And it was on a Thursday several years after this that our story begins.

MINUTES OF THE SIXTH ANNUAL GENERAL MEETING OF "THE GOODIES" HELD AT THE
ALBERT HALL ON THURSDAY 5th MAY
1977 AT 7.29 p.m. (G.M.T.)

PRESENT: Tim Brooke-Taylor
                  Graeme Garden
                  Bill Oddie
                  Andre Previn
                  The London Symphony Orchestra.

1.   TIM BROOKE-TAYLOR opened the meeting, as Chairman, by welcoming
      the L.S.O. and their audience. He said, during the slow movement
      of Beethoven's 5th, that he didn't want to put a damper on the
      proceedings, but the Hall had been pre-booked by the Goodies for
      their A.G.M. and that he himself had checked with the vicar only
      the previous evening.

      He then went on to shout that the Goodies were always willing to
      compromise and that he proposed that their A.G.M. should be
      transferred to Cricklewood. He asked for someone to second this.
      A man of indeterminate sex bellowed "Pardon" from the Gallery,
      and a Lady of very determined sex screamed "Certainly, first
      right and follow the lino", from the Royal Box.
      The motion was eventually seconded by the third violinist from
      the left, the one with the dodgy wig, and carried by a majority
      of two thousand and ninety eight votes to three, with the brass
      section abstaining. The Goodies then returned several times to
      the platform for a standing ovation culminating in the presentat-
      ion of many bunches of flowers which Mr Andre Previn kindly
      accepted on their behalf.

2. THE DERBY AND JOAN KUNG FOO AND MASSAGE PARLOR, CRICKLEWOOD.
8.17 p.m. G.M.T.

The Chairman re-opened the meeting by welcoming Mr Oddie, and
Mr Garden to this Extraordinary General Meeting of the Goodies.
Bill Oddie objected to the word extraordinary as it seemed
pretty (expletive deleted) ordinary to him. Graeme Garden said
that he had no particular views on the subject but if he was being
pressed for an opinion, which he was and would they please stop
it, then he would have to say that the meeting was pink. The
Chairman then proposed that it should be called: A Not Entirely
Ordinary Pink General Meeting. (ANEOPGM).
This was agreed.

ADOPTION OF MINUTES. The Chairman then asked Mr Garden if he could read
the minutes of the last meeting. Mr Garden said he couldn't.
Mr Oddie and Mr Brooke-Taylor said they couldn't either. It was
agreed however that they looked a bit like"Squiggle squiggle
Chemist. Squiggle squiggle (something that looked a bit like a
cow sitting on a stool) squiggle Lady Antonia Fraser squiggle

(cont)... squiggle little bits of tomato squiggle all over the
rhubarb patch". These minutes were unanimously adopted.
Bill agreed to the possibility of setting them to music.

THE CHAIRMAN'S REPORT. The Chairman apologised and said that it must
have been something he'd eaten.

ELECTION OF NEW CHAIRMAN: When the music stopped Bill Oddie was in the
chair. B.O. objected to the 'Male Chauvinist' title of Chairman
and suggested 'Chairperson'.
T.B-T. thought 'Chairthing' would be more appropiate.
This motion was carried 2 to 1.
G.G. requested that the phrase 'Motion Carried' should not be
used in future as this reminded him of his days as a medical
student.
T.B-T. was then elected Treasurer.

TREASURER'S REPORT. See Chairman's Report

THE FUTURE. The Chairthing requested that the aims and objectives of
the Goodies as contained in the Articles of Association should
be re-circulated as the one thing that was of paramount interest
to all members was 'What do we do now?'.
G.G. congratulated the new Chairthing on his constructive and
incisive statement, made all the more impressive by the fact
that he'd done it without moving his lips.
T.B-T. also congratulated the Chairthing and added that he
couldn't have put it better himself - exactly the same but
certainly not better.
The Aims and Objectives were then circulated.

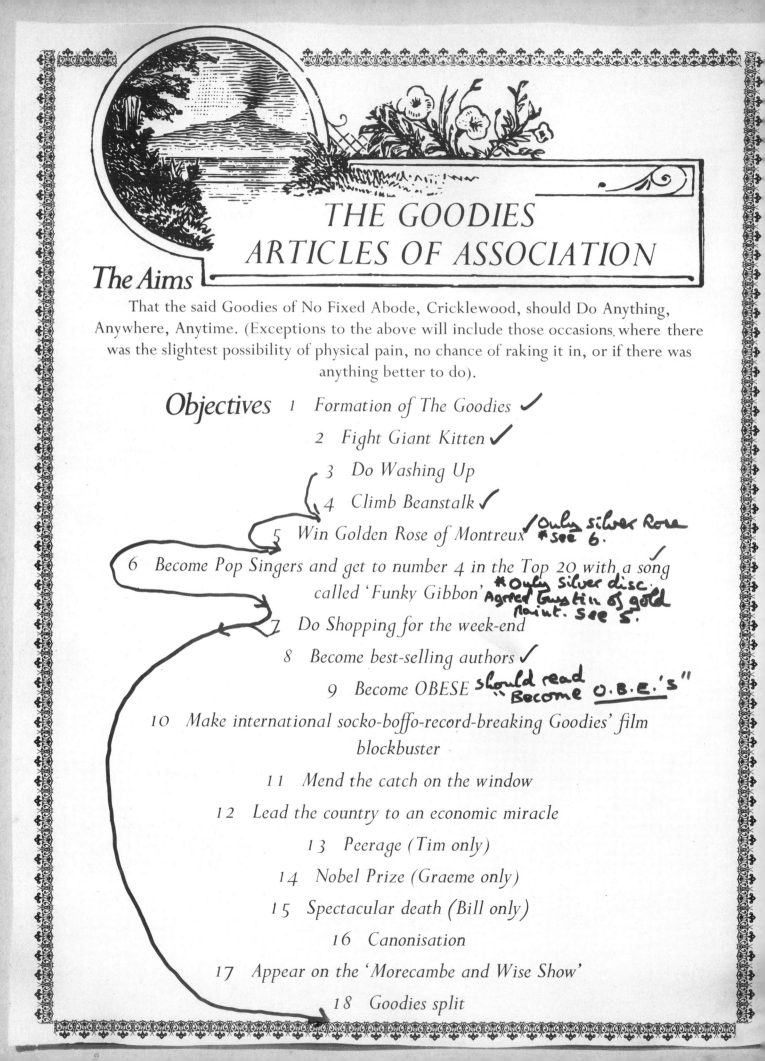

THE GOODIES
ARTICLES OF ASSOCIATION

The Aims

That the said Goodies of No Fixed Abode, Cricklewood, should Do Anything, Anywhere, Anytime. (Exceptions to the above will include those occasions where there was the slightest possibility of physical pain, no chance of raking it in, or if there was anything better to do).

Objectives

1 Formation of The Goodies ✓

2 Fight Giant Kitten ✓

3 Do Washing Up

4 Climb Beanstalk ✓

5 Win Golden Rose of Montreux ✓ *Only silver Rose* *see 6.*

6 Become Pop Singers and get to number 4 in the Top 20 with a song called 'Funky Gibbon' ✓ *Only silver disc. Agreed swustin of gold Paint. see 5.*

7 Do Shopping for the week-end

8 Become best-selling authors ✓

9 Become OBESE *should read "Become O.B.E.'s"*

10 Make international socko-boffo-record-breaking Goodies' film blockbuster

11 Mend the catch on the window

12 Lead the country to an economic miracle

13 Peerage (Tim only)

14 Nobel Prize (Graeme only)

15 Spectacular death (Bill only)

16 Canonisation

17 Appear on the 'Morecambe and Wise Show'

18 Goodies split

T.B-T. apologised for his lack of success on item 9. He reported
that his contact at the Palace had unfortunately been 'indisposed'.
He had in fact fallen off his ladder and was now no longer able
to clean the Royal windows. He was happy to report, however, that
his contact had described to him in graphic detail the sight that had
caused him to fall from his ladder. T.B-T felt confident,
therefore that he could rely on a peerage at the very least merely
for keeping his mouth shut. The fact that it was Jubilee Year
could only help. He then proposed the bringing forward of Item 13.

B.O. wished to remind T.B-T that he could only speak 'through the
chair', and that while he was at it he might as well stand on one
leg and use a funny voice. He then added "By Gum, this Chairthing business is fun".

T.B-T refusing to speak through the chair or anything else for
that matter said that if B.O. was unwilling to take anything
seriously they might as well bring forward item 15 with the view
to implementing it immediately. He also expressed the view that
this be done slowly, using such things as garden shears and red
hot pokers.

G.G. While agreeing with T.B-T's feelings felt that it would be
best to stick to the original order of Objectives as he was
rather hoping that Item 14 and for that matter Item 15 would
coincide with Christmas. He therefore proposed that the Goodies
should make an International Socko Boffo Record Breaking Film
Blockbuster. By Friday.

A FILM   T.B-T wished it to be recorded that although he was against the
idea of making a film ('All those early mornings') he had no
objections to being a film star. He had always wanted to wear
dark glasses, carry a poodle and be rude to waiters.
G.G. pointed out that you had to make a film to be a film star.
T.B-T. pointed out that this was not the case and quoted as
evidence Britt Ekland, Jackie Collins and Bianca Jagger.

B.O. pointed out that T.B-T. had worn dark glasses,
carried a poodle and been rude to waiters. No one had considered
him to be a filmstar then. He also pointed out that due to the
dark glasses T.B-T. had been unable to see that the waiters had,
in revenge, cooked and served his poodle.
T.B-T. screamed 'So that's what did it!' (SEE CHAIRMAN'S REPORT
AND TREASURER'S REPORT).

MATTERS ARISING. Poodle a l'orange.
In the absence of T.B-T. it was decided to make a film.
G.G. would look out his book on film making.

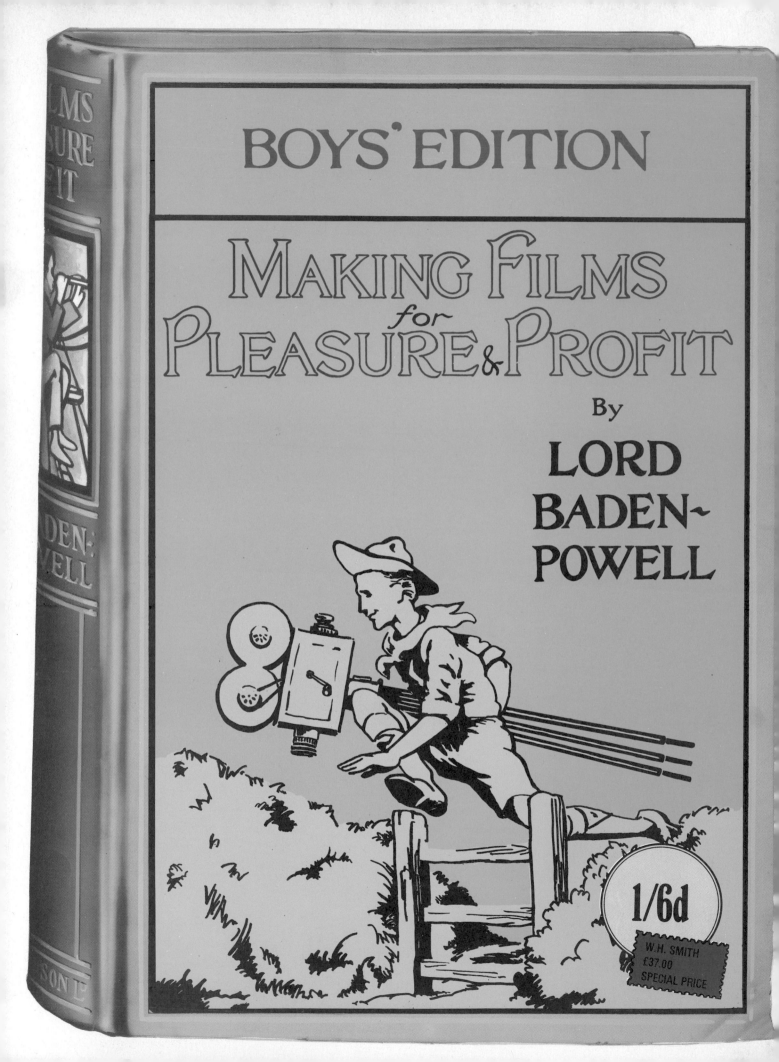

CHAPTER TWO
FINDING THE PRODUCER

Every Motion Picture *must have a Producer*; although nobody knows quite what a Producer does. However, you must have one, and that's all there is to it. You probably do not know a Producer yourself, as they rarely circulate in respectable society, so it may be necessary to advertise for one (after a cold shower of course!)
Lord Baden-Powell

An extract from *Making Films for Pleasure and Profit* by Lord Baden-Powell

Within a week, the advertisement placed by the Goodies in the Newsagent's window brought a flood of eager enquiries ... sadly, none of them from Film Producers. But word was beginning to spread throughout the Motion Picture industry, and on the morning of Monday, February 18th at 0927 hours, a slim envelope slid on to the doormat – an envelope whose contents were soon to be revealed ...

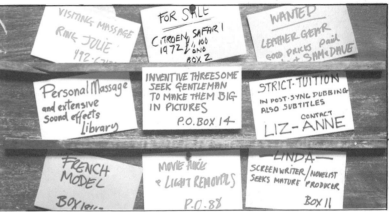

Wardour Street! Bustling hub of Britain's Movie universe!
Wardour Street! London's answer to Hollywood's Broadway!
Wardour Street! Europe's Burbank!
But, most important of all at that moment . . . Wardour Street! Home of Louie Bunce Productions, Inc.

Bunce House has a modest facade, and it was only after two hours cycling up and down the street that Tim, Bill and Graeme managed to spot their destination. In fact, they were only able to recognise it by the sign announcing *The Home of Louie Bunce Productions Inc.* which they found beside the bell, between the bells marked *Tina* and the one labelled *New Ugandan Model – second floor. Walk up.* Having decided to ring the middle bell, they were let in by an Entryphone, and made their way up the grimy stairs to the office of the man who was to become the Producer of their film – the legendary Louie Bunce.

Bunce House, Wardour Street – the home of Louie Bunce Productions.

The legendary film producer, Louie Bunce.

Louie Bunce pictured here with long-time business associate, usually just referred to as 'the Don' – although nobody knows which University.

Louie Bunce welcomed them warmly and locked the door behind them. He agreed that there was no real need for them to sign a blank contract at this stage. He offered them a cigar, and when they accepted, he cut it into three equal pieces and gave it to them. Then they asked him what a Film Producer *actually does*.

For a moment, Bunce turned pale and damp. Then, summoning up the wiles developed in a lifetime's free-wheeling and double-dealing, he spoke . . .

"Boys . . . I've kicked around in this business a long time. I was brought up in this neighbourhood. Soho, that's my home. Look out that window – that back alleyway there, that's where my family lived in those days. That alleyway was home to me. Look at it. No, ignore the grey-haired old lady waving at us – she's most probably somebody else's mother.

But you know boys, when I was a kid, my momma used to say to me 'Louie, all day you'r under my feet, why don't you get out more? Go down the street like all the other kids and produce a few movies. Would it hurt you to re-make Gone with the Wind?'

"My son, the producer." Mrs Miriam Bunce

Well I took her advice, and that's how I started in this game. And I love it. Every penny of it. But times have changed, tastes have altered, the public know what they want. And that's what we've got to give them.

The Goodies and Louie Bunce – first impressions

What can we say?

Suggestions are put forward

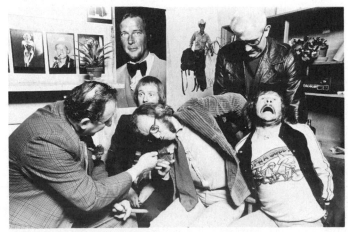

Differences are ironed out

It's a deal!

Nowadays, your cinemagoers are much more sophisticated. They want pictures of bare bums and tits, and mucky language. Sophistication, that's the name of the game. Once upon a time you worked to a simple formula – boy meets girl. Well nowadays, I mean it's girl meets girl, boy meets boy, two girls meet boy, nun meets goat, you see what I'm getting at? But nobody wants to take a risk do they? Nobody wants to be a pathfinder. Which is why we restrict ourselves to the follow-up market. What you call the Spinoff. What we call the Ripoff.

Right now we're working on a 'Confessions of' rip-off. One with a bit of class though, one of the classics. We've just roughed out a treatment of The Confessions of Dorian Grey by Orson Wilde. Wonderful story – wonderful story, and a really good gimmick. Listen, you go to a 'Confession' Movie, and what do you see? Most of the time you're seeing nothing but the hero's bare bum, am I right? Now Robin's a talented actor – you know, what a performer! What range, what expression. Course he's not so good with his face, but that bum . . . it speaks volumes.

So, in our up-dated Dorian Grey, our hero has this portrait painted of his bum. You see? It's so beautiful, he has it captured on canvas. It's admired by society – great titled ladies visit his boudoir just to be dazzled by his bum. Now it's all very tasteful of course, none of your sophisticated post-cards muck. However, our Dorian embarks on a career of debauchery, and excess, in spite of which, for fifty years, his bum remains plump, pert and firm. But his bum's portrait in the attic – over the years it comes to show the ravages of sophistication.

Here's some of our promotional material to fill in the details.''

Louie Bunce presents

The Confessions of Dorian Grey

A LOUIE BUNCE
PRODUCTION

x

starring

Robin Askwith

as Dorian Grey

with

Albert Finney,
John Gielgud,
Frank Finlay

and

Nicholas Parsons
in a special guest appearance

A salute to the genius of
OSCAR WILDE—
the Benny Hill of his day

in BUNCECOLOR C

MUSIC BY BERNSTEIN
AND WOODWARD

SCREENPLAY BY
LOUIE BUNCE

BASED ON THE NOVEL BY
OSCAR WILDE

DIRECTED BY
BERNARD MANNING

Produced by
Louis Bunce

"His depravity
reached the very
bottom..."

LOUIE BUNCE SAYS,
"If you enjoy this—
wait till you see
Lady Windermere's Fan!"

MARGOT +
KEN COX

This was all very well and good, but before the Goodies could ask Bunce precisely what contribution *he* could make to *their* latest enterprise ...

"Boys," said Bunce, "this is ridiculous? How can we do business without a business lunch? We'll go and eat, Why not?"

As they were hungry, they agreed. When he asked them what sort of meal they fancied, they replied "Indian." And so it was that the three Goodies and Louie Bunce were among the first customers at the newly opened Indian restaurant – *The Teepee*.

As the waiters, resplendent in feathers and beadwork, served them with lunch, Louie finally agreed to produce the film, but only on condition that a contract was signed there and then, before they went to see anyone else. A contract was duly drawn up on the menu, and signed by those present.

Business completed, Louie Bunce insisted that, as a gesture of goodwill, the Goodies should pay for the lunch. This they did, and Louie even suggested that, as the red-indian waiters were in fact all film extras looking for work, they should leave a generous tip. Tim, in charge of the petty cash, payed for the lunch and left a largish sum in silver under his coffee cup. (Although the Goodies did not see it, Louie Bunce, already protecting their image and feeling that the sum left might still be thought too small by the waiters, saved the day by sliding the offending gratuity off the table and into his pocket. As it happens, none of the staff noticed, as the head-waiter was on the phone sorting out a dispute over reservations and the second waiter was looking after a diner who had impaled his tongue with a fork while eating wampum, and manfully restraining himself from remarking that "White man speaks with forked tongue ...")

Next morning, Tuesday, the Goodies received a letter
from Louie, which read:

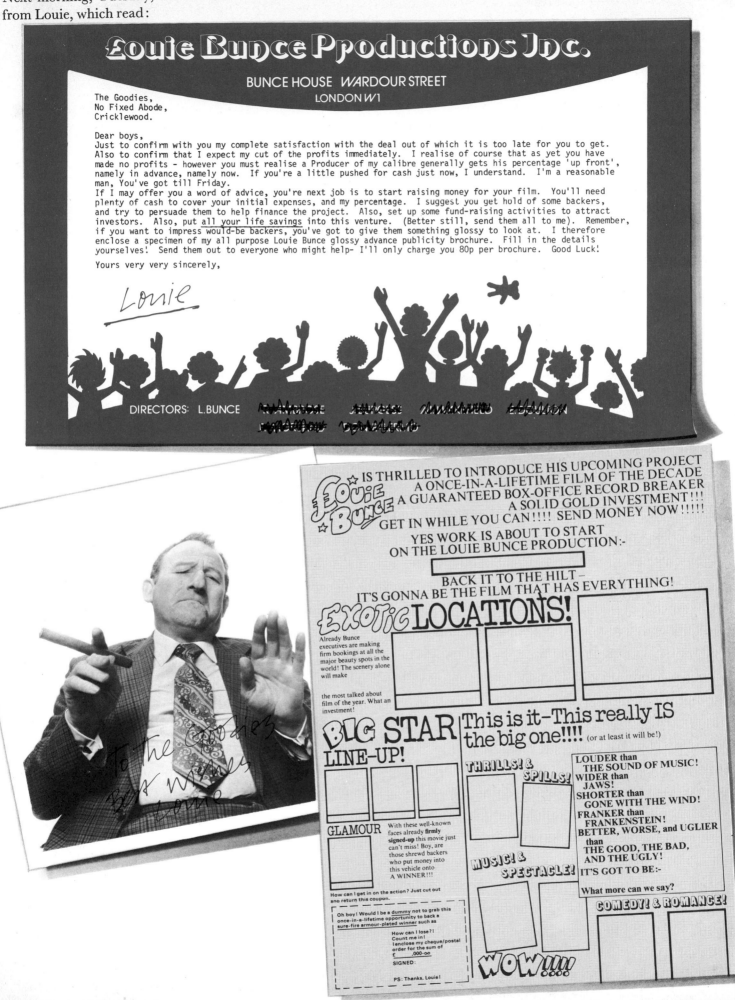

Louie Bunce Productions Inc.

BUNCE HOUSE *WARDOUR* STREET
LONDON *W*1

The Goodies,
No Fixed Abode,
Cricklewood.

Dear boys,
Just to confirm with you my complete satisfaction with the deal out of which it is too late for you to get.
Also to confirm that I expect my cut of the profits immediately. I realise of course that as yet you have
made no profits - however you must realise a Producer of my calibre generally gets his percentage 'up front',
namely in advance, namely now. If you're a little pushed for cash just now, I understand. I'm a reasonable
man, You've got till Friday.
If I may offer you a word of advice, you're next job is to start raising money for your film. You'll need
plenty of cash to cover your initial expenses, and my percentage. I suggest you get hold of some backers,
and try to persuade them to help finance the project. Also, set up some fund-raising activities to attract
investors. Also, put all your life savings into this venture. (Better still, send them all to me). Remember,
if you want to impress would-be backers, you've got to give them something glossy to look at. I therefore
enclose a specimen of my all purpose Louie Bunce glossy advance publicity brochure. Fill in the details
yourselves! Send them out to everyone who might help- I'll only charge you 80p per brochure. Good Luck!

Yours very very sincerely,

Louie

DIRECTORS: L.BUNCE ~~RKNICHOLS~~ ~~JEKCLEESE~~ ~~MUNDRFELD~~ ~~EJBURON~~ ~~MCDOWT~~ ~~OOMCKAVIO~~

*To The Goodies
Best Wishes,
Louie*

LOUIE BUNCE IS THRILLED TO INTRODUCE HIS UPCOMING PROJECT
A ONCE-IN-A-LIFETIME FILM OF THE DECADE
A GUARANTEED BOX-OFFICE RECORD BREAKER
A SOLID GOLD INVESTMENT !!!!
GET IN WHILE YOU CAN !!!! SEND MONEY NOW !!!!!
YES WORK IS ABOUT TO START
ON THE LOUIE BUNCE PRODUCTION :-

BACK IT TO THE HILT –
IT'S GONNA BE THE FILM THAT HAS EVERYTHING!

EXOTIC LOCATIONS!

Already Bunce
executives are making
firm bookings at all the
major beauty spots in the
world! The scenery alone
will make

the most talked about
film of the year. What an
investment!

BIG STAR LINE-UP!

This is it-This really IS the big one!!!! (or at least it will be!)

GLAMOUR With these well-known
faces already **firmly
signed-up** this movie just
can't miss! Boy, are
those shrewd backers
who put money into
this vehicle onto
A WINNER!!!

THRILLS! & SPILLS!

LOUDER than
THE SOUND OF MUSIC!
WIDER than
JAWS!
SHORTER than
GONE WITH THE WIND!
FRANKER than
FRANKENSTEIN!
BETTER, WORSE, and UGLIER
than
THE GOOD, THE BAD,
AND THE UGLY!
IT'S GOT TO BE:-

What more can we say?

MUSIC! & SPECTACLE!

How can I get in on the action? Just cut out
and return this coupon.

Oh boy! Would I be a **dummy** not to grab this
once-in-a-lifetime opportunity to back a
sure-fire armour-plated winner such as

How can I lose?!
Count me in!
I enclose my cheque/postal
order for the sum of
£ ,000-00
SIGNED:

PS: Thanks, Louie!

COMEDY! & ROMANCE!

WOW!!!!

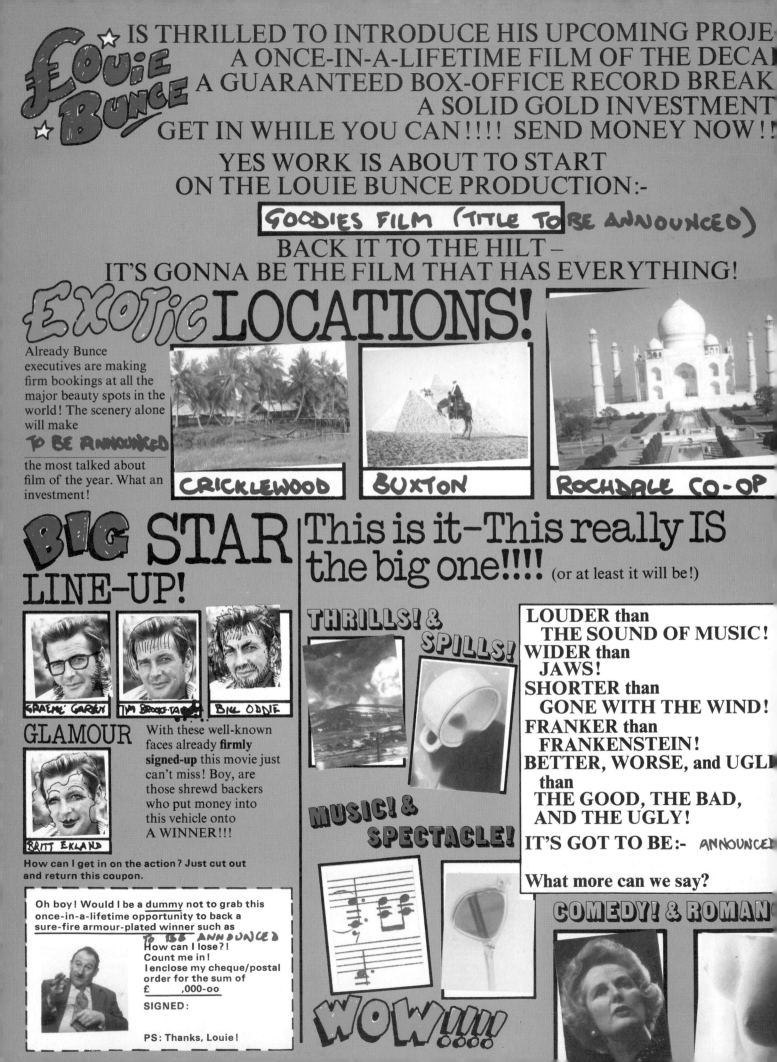

£OUIE BUNCE IS THRILLED TO INTRODUCE HIS UPCOMING PROJE...
A ONCE-IN-A-LIFETIME FILM OF THE DECA...
A GUARANTEED BOX-OFFICE RECORD BREAK...
A SOLID GOLD INVESTMENT...
GET IN WHILE YOU CAN!!!! SEND MONEY NOW!!...

YES WORK IS ABOUT TO START
ON THE LOUIE BUNCE PRODUCTION:-

GOODIES FILM (TITLE TO BE ANNOUNCED)

BACK IT TO THE HILT –
IT'S GONNA BE THE FILM THAT HAS EVERYTHING!

EXOTIC LOCATIONS!

Already Bunce executives are making firm bookings at all the major beauty spots in the world! The scenery alone will make TO BE ANNOUNCED the most talked about film of the year. What an investment!

CRICKLEWOOD

BUXTON

ROCHDALE CO-OP

BIG STAR LINE-UP!

GRAEME GARDEN

TIM BROOKE-TAYLOR

BILL ODDIE

GLAMOUR

BRITT EKLAND

With these well-known faces already **firmly signed-up** this movie just can't miss! Boy, are those shrewd backers who put money into this vehicle onto A WINNER!!!

How can I get in on the action? Just cut out and return this coupon.

Oh boy! Would I be a dummy not to grab this once-in-a-lifetime opportunity to back a sure-fire armour-plated winner such as TO BE ANNOUNCED
How can I lose?!
Count me in!
I enclose my cheque/postal order for the sum of
£   ,000-oo

SIGNED:

PS: Thanks, Louie!

This is it-This really IS the big one!!!! (or at least it will be!)

THRILLS! & SPILLS!

MUSIC! & SPECTACLE!

WOW!!!!

LOUDER than
THE SOUND OF MUSIC!
WIDER than
JAWS!
SHORTER than
GONE WITH THE WIND!
FRANKER than
FRANKENSTEIN!
BETTER, WORSE, and UGL...
than
THE GOOD, THE BAD,
AND THE UGLY!
IT'S GOT TO BE:- ANNOUNCE...

What more can we say?

COMEDY! & ROMAN...

CHAPTER THREE
RAISING THE MONEY

Raising the money is by far and away the most important and *artistic* part of film-making. Indeed, I often tell boys who wish to accumulate capital for the financing of some pet project the tale of two niggers.

Many years ago in the lovely Transvaal, Lt-Col 'Podge' Bulstrode had a couple of nigger-boy servants, one of whom was lamentably lazy, whilst the other was of an industrious nature. After fifty years of faithful service, they were both rewarded with the traditional penny, for which they both expressed their traditional gratitude.

"And what will you do with your pennies, nigger-boys?" asked their master, the Lt-Col.

"Well *baas*," replied the lazy nigger, "I will put my penny in a hole in the ground, lest any man try to steal it. In this way, when I die, I shall still have my penny safe and sound!"

"I, on the other hand," exclaimed the industrious nigger, "shall invest my penny, and thereby shall I increase my wealth by another penny, which likewise I shall invest, and speculating thus, *baas*, I shall raise much money, with a view to funding an entirely independent motion-picture production, *aieee!* – yea, a box-office wow which will ensure that I become the richest and most respected movie mogul in the whole of my village!"

"Well said, nigger boy!" ejaculated 'Podge' Bulstrode. "The cold baths are on me!"

I cannot help but feel that there is a lesson for us all in this yarn. And by the by, the name of that industrious nigger was M'Boko Poitier (no relation).

Lord Baden-Powell

An extract from **Making Films for Pleasure and Profit** by Lord Baden-Powell

The Goodies fund-raising sub-committee first met on May 19th in the Luxurious plushness of the elegant Suez room at London's exclusive انات نفط خام في ميناء الفحل (Dorchester Hotel.)

This was the thrifty threesome's first taste of the sort of high living usually associated with the world of movie-making, and they were enjoying it. Doing things in style was going to be O.K. by them, they thought, as they lay back on the priceless rugs and cushions, scoffing platefuls of Turkish Delight, sipping sherbet, and puffing contentedly at the traditional Hubble-bubble pipe, or Hookah, which made them feel very happy (hence the phrase 'the happy hubble-bubble.')

Well, self indulgence is all very well, but there was business to attend to, and a basic approach to the problem of raising funds was rapidly sketched out on the bus on the way home. It was unanimously agreed by all three (except for Bill, Graeme abstaining) that they should follow the example set out by B–P himself in his invaluable appendix (iii), and a list of projects was made out there and then. The meeting was adjourned just after Marble Arch.

LIST OF PROJECTS

Project 1

Project 2

Project 3

Project 4

Project 5

ETC

At a second meeting five weeks later, the three would-be movie moguls discussed their progress so far. In fact the situation was very pleasing. At first they had been tempted to try the pre-selling technique – basing their campaign on the merchandising of spin-off products (T-shirts, books, records, etc etc.). This approach had of course paid off in the past. In cosmetics alone a major marketing impact was made by the sales of such movie-oriented products as 'Dracula' Tooth-Powder, 'Deep Throat' Lip Gloss, 'Shampoo' Shampoo, 'Emmanuelle' Tissues, and of course 'Texas Chain Saw' Mascara.

This was not for the Goodies.

Their campaign was to consist of a series of well-timed, well-publicized, and hard-hitting Jumble Sales, Fetes, Coffee Mornings, Raffles, and Begging Letters. (A technique, incidentally, pioneered by an earlier block-busting smasheroo!)

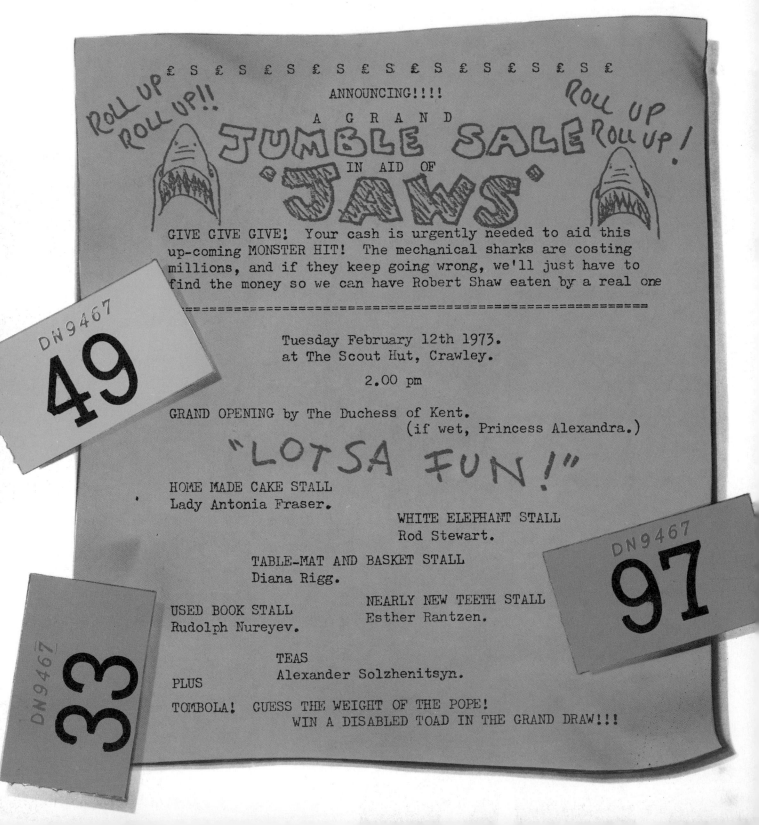

£$£$£$£$£$£$£$£$£$£$£$£$£

ROLL UP ROLL UP!!
ROLL UP ROLL UP!

ANNOUNCING!!!!
A GRAND
JUMBLE SALE
IN AID OF
'JAWS'

GIVE GIVE GIVE! Your cash is urgently needed to aid this up-coming MONSTER HIT! The mechanical sharks are costing millions, and if they keep going wrong, we'll just have to find the money so we can have Robert Shaw eaten by a real one

===

Tuesday February 12th 1973.
at The Scout Hut, Crawley.

2.00 pm

GRAND OPENING by The Duchess of Kent.
                    (if wet, Princess Alexandra.)

"LOTSA FUN!"

HOME MADE CAKE STALL
Lady Antonia Fraser.

                    WHITE ELEPHANT STALL
                    Rod Stewart.

        TABLE-MAT AND BASKET STALL
        Diana Rigg.

USED BOOK STALL   NEARLY NEW TEETH STALL
Rudolph Nureyev.   Esther Rantzen.

                TEAS
                Alexander Solzhenitsyn.
PLUS

TOMBOLA! GUESS THE WEIGHT OF THE POPE!
         WIN A DISABLED TOAD IN THE GRAND DRAW!!!

DN9467
49

DN9467
97

DN9467
33

For the Goodies, the *Jaws* approach paid off.

The money was soon rolling in, thanks to the invaluable help of the local Boy Scouts (Slug Patrol), the members of the Women's Institute, the Men's Institute, the staff and pupils of the King Herod Infants' School, the Girl Guides, the Cubs, the Brownies, the Darkies, and of course Mrs Godzilla who made the teas.

The generosity of the investors was touching, and in no time at all the contributions came to a staggering total of Two Million Pounds! (almost five thousand dollars!) Having raised what they thought to be an adequate budget, the Goodies wrote immediately to Louie Bunce, asking him what should be their next move.

Four days later they received a reverse-charges telegram from Mr Bunce, who was at that time enjoying a well-earned holiday as a guest of Mme. President Tole of Venezuela. His joy was limitless, and on page six of the telegram he insisted that the Goodies should throw a "Thank you" party for all those who had contributed to the cause. The elation was infectious, and that very Saturday saw the Goodies playing host at a glittering get-together of investors, a real slap-up knock-down humdinger of a function, thrown in the 'Watership Down' suite of London's Playboy Club.

Came the dawn . . .

PLAYBOY CLUB.

(Goodies 'Thankyou for the Money' Party)

I N V O I C E

	£
Hire of suite	500.00
Food	750.00
Drink	3,275.00
Breakages (General)	12.83
Breakages (Mr Moon)	11,765,15
To Mending lift	2,500.00
To Mending roof	5,250.00
To Mending Park Lane	375,000.07
To Mending Miss World	375,000,08
To Mending Electronic Calculator	55555555.55
Mr Randy Newman (cabaret)	25.00 (plus meal)
Mr G. Melly (porterage)	;8.20
Miss V. Redgrave (settled out of court	900.00 (plus meal)
Bribes to police	150.00
" to Noise Abatement Society	750.00
" to Traffic Wardens	6.00
Cover charge	0.45
Service	700.50
VAT (at 8¾%)	200,000 .00
VAT (at 834%)	1,765,998 .04

TOTAL=========================== TWO MILLION QUID

At a third meeting of the fund-raising sub-committee it was agreed that the Party had been a great success, and that a good time had been had by one and all, and that it had cost the £2,000,000.00 they had raised.

The matter of raising a similar sum once again to finance the projected Goodies film was brought up. It was decided to look on the bright side. It was also decided to don thinking caps and come up with more suggestions.

So it was that, in the following weeks, some of the wealthiest people in the world were approached with a request to contribute some of their hard-inherited savings to bolster up the ailing British film industry. In return for their investment in the Goodies planned box-office-record-buster, they were promised a degree of control over the picture, and were allowed to impose conditions. . .

Sheikh Yafist	£100,000	Film must star Rita Acapulco.
Mrs. Brooke-Taylor (Tim's mum)	50p	Tim must do his little imitation of Auntie Pru - with the hat!
BRYAN FORBES	£200	I want to play the role seaman who cracks under pressure
The Frightfully Decent Good Old British Loan Company Limited	£50,000	Immediate repayments plus 300% interest, or the 'Frightfully Decent' League of Chums will pop round for a cup of tea and your toe-nails
Sir Denis Vauxhall -Viva	£15,000	Hero must drive a Vauxhall - Viva
Baron Klaus Jensen - Interceptor	£10,000	Hero must drive a Jensen Interceptor
Lady Morphy Richards	£10,000	Hero must drive a Morphy Richards
Earl of Marwood	£20,000	Only if you cast Miss Rita Aca as the lead. She's a poppet!

...of Cinema Critics ...cola Co	£5,000 £5,000	Film must contain references of Marty Feldman Movie to be retitled: "Drink Coca-cola!"
...nch of Rhine	£20,000	No belly-dancers, or camel jokes. (must star miss Rita Acapulco) Movie to be retitled 'Don't Drink Coca-Cola'
...psi-Cola Company	£5,000	I want to play Bryan Forbes
...Richard Attenborough		
...ndersmere and Bruston Surgical ...ss and Appliance Manufacturing Co	£1000	Hero must be seen to wear (and enjoy) many of our invaluable aids. It's time people realized that there is nothing to sniggerr at in a truss. These simple devices, thoughtfully employed, bring pleasure to hundreds, and we enclose a copy of the words and music of our company song "I'm tickled to death with my truss" This number should feature in your films, sung on several occasions by your hero. I don't know if you have considered approaching Frank Sinatra for the role, but P.T.O.

After two whirlwind months, the Goodies once again had money to make a movie. Things were looking good, although on his return a bronzed Louie Bunce pointed out that they only had the money on condition that the film was shot on location at 73 separate Holiday Hotels, featured prominently 25 domestic appliances and 43 different makes of car, didn't poke fun at the Mafia, Israel, Lady Falkender, OPEC, or very rich people in general, and that it starred no less than 800 up and coming young actresses, and one young actor recommended for his sensitive handling of featured parts. However Mr Bunce saw no great problem in this situation, and was heartened by Tim's news that he had found the hat.

All systems were go!

CHAPTER FOUR
FINDING THE DIRECTOR

Finding a director is no granny knot. Directors are nearly as important as scoutmasters – so the Sunday papers tell us. After taking your cold shower learn to spot a director. This is easily done as they all wear jodhpurs and have their hats on back to front. To find a director simply follow the tracks of his broken marriages. If you think you can do it by yourself, take another cold shower and think again.

Lord Baden-Powell

An extract from Making Films for Pleasure and Profit by Lord Baden-Powell

Tim Brooke-Taylor takes up the story with an extract from his journal dated April 5th.

April 5th. Well if Lord B–P. says we need a director then I suppose we must have one. Personally I can't see why I couldn't do it all myself. When I'm better, of course, and this cold has gone. Could it be all these cold showers? However if we do need one, who? Well obviously we want to make a nice film for all the family, with lots of incredibly nice people and cuddly animals, so where better than the Walt Disney Studios? Unfortunately I found that my expenses wouldn't quite reach to California. Actually they wouldn't even have got me to New York. They might have got me to Harlesden, but I wrote instead.

Dear Timbrook,

Gee, Mr Disney would sure love to make your little film but he's like, dead, see. His successor, Mr Michael Mouse, has asked me to say that since his retirement as an actor, movies are a dead duck. Come to think of it, since Mr Mouse has put out a contract to his ex colleague and arch rival, a movie about a dead duck might not be such a bad idea.

However, he suggests that, in your case, what you need instead of a movie is a Disney ~~Rip Off~~ Entertainment Unit: Number One. (Disneyland).

I am enclosing a poster for our new attractions at Disney Entertainment Unit.

Here's pixie dust in your eye.

Yours Percival Luto

P. LUTO

DISNEY LAND

HOW THE WEST WAS WON
<u>You become a pioneer.</u>

REAL BULLETS
REAL INDIANS
...RY WHILE STOCKS LAST.

A VISIT TO THE WHITE HOUSE
FAIL THE LIE DETECTOR TEST AND BECOME – PRESIDENT!

Free Peanuts
DENTISTS : HALF PRICE.

Press the Button

THE DEPRESSION
See what it was really like in Grandpa's day.

<u>SCREAM</u> With laughter as he loses all his money.

<u>HOWL</u> With merriment as he gets thinner and thinner.

<u>RUPTURE</u> yourself with mirth as he jumps from the top of the Empire State Building.

IT'S TERRIFYINGLY FUNNY

If you enjoyed THE DEPRESSION see it happening now in

A Trip to Britain

..EE the Limeys, they're real cute.

..OW them cents and watch them scramble.

...the thrills and spills of the Pound at the Krazee BANK OF ENGLAND.

...SED

ZAP
THE CONG
Just like Dad. But this time we win

A village destroyed <u>every</u> trip.

<u>PLUS</u> "GOOFY GOES MAD."

MAKE YOUR OWN HAMBURGER

<u>REAL COWS</u> catch them yourself.

GUNS AXES & BUNS all provided.

IT'S AN EDUCATION

Tim's journal

To be honest I felt sick – sick as a pig. Now there's an idea, a movie about a pig being sick. Oh dear I think it's catching. Perhaps Graeme will have better luck with Alfred Hitchcock. Louie Bunce has just rung from Los Angeles to ask how everything was going which was very nice of him. After that I was only too happy to collect his suit from the cleaners. They were very concerned that they hadn't been able to get all the red paint out of the jacket. They hadn't apparently come across that sort of paint before. Mr Bunce reversed the charges for tax reasons.

On Wednesday, April 5th, Graeme Garden visited veteran film director and master of the thriller, Alfred Hitchcock. The words are by Graeme Garden. The pictures are by Alf Hitchcock himself.

Tim's Journal continues

3 p.m. Oh dear, what are we going to do? I know! At least he's British and it's not really dirty is it? Just good clean English smut. Bawdy – that's the word.

5 p.m. I was wrong, horribly wrong. This is what happened . . .

Posing as a film journalist I visited Peter 'Carry On' Rogers. Peter was filming on the backlot at Shepperton. A scene was in progress.

Sadly I didn't think this was quite what we wanted; so like any good journalist I made my excuses and left.

CARRY ON CHRIST

A PETER ROGERS FIL

TODAY FISH & BREAD! SORRY NO CHIPS

MOTHER'S PRIDE

"CARRY ON CHRIST" SHOT 24: THE FEEDING OF THE FIVE THOUSAND. TAKE 23

KENNETH CONNOR: Crikey, you've got a big one!
(St Peter Out)

KENNETH WILLIAMS: I beg your pardon!
(St John & St Thomas)

HATTIE JACQUES: Are you going to cut it into little pieces?
(The Five Thousand)

CHARLES HAWTREY: Cor, that sounds painful.
(A wise virgin)

KENNETH WILLIAMS: Madam, we are talking about my loaf.
(As above)

BARBARA WINDSOR: Blimey, I've never heard it called that before.
(Not a wise virgin) 'Ere mind what you're doing with my pretzels.

JOAN SIMS: Pardon 'er French. Of course everyone knows you
(Judith Iscarriat) can buy five Sunblest loaves and still have
                    have change from thirty pieces of silver.

ORSON WELLES: Yes Sunblest, the people who always have a
(God Voice Over only) bun in the oven. Ooops, know what I mean.

Bill Oddie takes up the story

Apparently we needed a director. But who?

Well obviously we wanted a film with lots of blood and guts and people being smashed to pieces and tortured and strung up on telegraph poles. And obviously we wanted some real ear splitting, mind blowing, heavy heavy music. But who could do that as well as me? It was at that moment that we received our first really lucky break.

At 5.30 on Thursday, May the fourth, Bill received this mysterious message:

I am a film director in distress. Please come at midnight tonight, to save me.

You'll find me at 'The Castle', Weybridge.

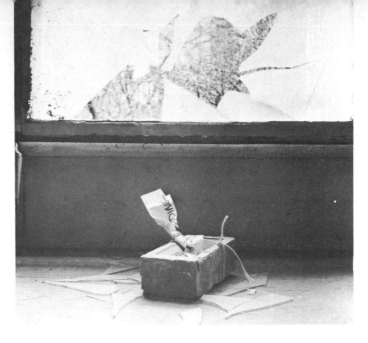

Bill Oddie takes up the story once more

Well I went there. It was real brass monkey weather. I had just changed my mind and was about to see if there was anything on at Ronnie Scott's when, on the stroke of midnight, the drawbridge crashed down. I crossed the bridge and came to an enormous wooden doorway. There was a sign 'Dun-Nun'. I suppose I should have realised who the mysterious stranger was then. I looked around. The walls were old with Ivy crawling up them. At least I think it was Ivy 'cos she had an all girl band with her. At that moment the doors swung open and Oliver Reed shot past me. I'm glad he missed.

"What do you want?" he said "and before you answer that I'd better tell you I'm a star. Without me the British Film Industry would be nothing".

I think he was a bit shy. But there was no doubt I was in the presence of someone rather special. I had met Keith Moon once, in what remained of the Savoy Hotel, and only he had ever affected me in the same way that Oliver Reed did now. I was sick in the moat.

At that moment the Moon came out and they both linked arms and danced away into the night.

I crept through the big doors and came into a huge hall. There were nuns everywhere; big nuns, small nuns, some as big as your head. Now it was obvious who my film director in distress was. I looked across the hall and there, sure enough, was the Mother Superior himself – Ken Russell.

He beckoned me over, looked me up and down and said "You're too big".

Too big! Nobody's ever called me that before. Well they have but not quite in this context.

"I want real midgets" he went on. "They keep sending me small men but I want midgets. Dwarves would do, in fact dwarves would do very well. Damn Fellini, he's got them all, he's cornered the market, he's got a Dwarf mountain, you can't get a Dwarf for love nor money." I tried to sympathise but he wouldn't be stopped. "Alright so I've got all the nuns , but how can you make a meaningful film about real life without dwarves? Damn him, he won't even do swaps".

I coughed. "Excuse me, you wanted to see me I believe". It was a funny sort of cough.

"Did I?" he said. "What do you do then?"

I coughed again "well you know, I write a bit, act a bit and compose a few songs, that sort of thing".

Suddenly he was interested, "A composer eh! Have I ever made a film about you?" I said he hadn't.

"Then you're not a composer. You're not a composer 'til I've filmed your life. Who'd ever heard of Elgar, Tchaikovsky or Lizst before I filmed *their* lives, eh? Who'd ever heard of Banatti?" I told him I'd never heard of Banatti.

"Well there you are then, I haven't made that one yet. I don't suppose you'd consider having your legs let in a little would you, I've never done a dwarf composer? No? Well I can't say I blame you. Any chance you want a film directed?"

I nodded. "You do!" With a flash he was off his throne and licking my shoes. "Oh Almighty one let me direct your film. I know I can't give you dwarves but I can give you anything else, anything."

Well it was soon settled. He'd be with us in two weeks, just as soon as he'd finished filming his commercial. It was for tobacco, he explained, and he was having a little trouble with the manufacturers.

"*Three* Nuns" he said contemptuously, "Now a Thousand Nuns, there you'd have a commercial."

I quietly let myself out, thinking how extraordinary the whole episode had been with not one "You'll soon get into the habit" joke.

Still, there was plenty of time.

So it was to be Ken Russell. Tim made one last desperate attempt to stop the inevitable.

Tim's Journal: March 8th.

Anything but Ken Russell. No. Anything but Sam Peckinpah and *then* Ken Russell. So I rang Roger Vadim to see if he could make it.

"Oui, Oui" he said. At least that's what I thought he'd said, but apparently he'd been speaking English as he rang off immediately.

When he rang back he said:

"Ma share Team, arm sore Dee's dressed, Bert our Ken not Mick, ow use hay? Lay Bons-Bons feel'em."

Well he may have been distressed, but I wanted to know why he couldn't make 'The Goodies' film. He told me he was busy making a scent commercial with his new wife. At least he assumed she would soon be his new I congratulated him and rang off. He had reversed the charges.

EST CE QUE LA REINE DE L'ANGLETERRE EST FINIE?

2,50 F

Suisse : 1,80 FS. Canada : 80 cts. Italie : 450 L. Angleterre : 30 p. Mar. : 2,90 D. Espagne : 40 pesetas. Belgique : 20 FB.

France Dimanche

LA PLUS FORTE VENTE DES HEBDOS D'INFORMATION EN FRANCE   31, rue du Louvre, 75002 PARIS. Tél. : 500-28-00

N° 1587 Semaine du 31 janvier au 6 février 1977

ELISABETH et PHILIP
Un terrible drame conjugal

LES 10 PREMIERES FEMMES

1ère
2ème
3ème
4ème
5ème
6ème
7ème
8ème
9ème
10ème

?

LONDRES, CHAQUE JOUR

NOUS n'avons pas en France une monarchie et peût-etre en Angleterre ils verront bientôt la lumière, et ils seront dans le même bateau que nous.

Nous savons que La Reine est très triste avec son mari, le prince Philip. Le Prince, évidemment, aime les garçons de scouting et La Reine Elizabeth est une amie très bonne, de Quintin Cochon (Lord Hailsham). Comme nous disons en Francais, "Il n'ya pas de fumée sans feu." (A continuer chaque jour dans ce journal)

La Reine est triste ?

ROGER VADIM VA SE MARIER ENCORE UNE FOIS. Roger Vadim a dit ce matin qu'il est très content avec sa dixième femme.

PARIS, LUNDI

Il ne savait pas son nom mais il a dit "Ma femme a les tits extraordinaires et encore une fois je suis tres content." Le prochain film de Monsieur Vadim sera 'Les Confessions d' un Dentiste Arabique Sur Le Travail'. Le Shah dê Rhaine , un bon ami du gouvernement de France suppliera l'argent pour ce film. Le Shah a dit qu'il ne veut pas aucune plaisanterie au sujet de camels ni de danseuses de l'estomac.

CHAPTER FIVE
CASTING

There were these two Pakis. One of them was a boy scout. Now I wouldn't say he was lazy but old ladies used to help *him* across the road. It was ten years before he found out where the front door was. He only gave up smoking 'cos the matches were out of his reach.

But there was this other Paki. Now he was a good Paki. He went back to his own country.

In India, or Pakistan as it is sometimes called, they have a caste system. Everyone knows their place. The same should apply when casting your film. The hero must always be well dressed with nice clean shoes. The villain must have a funny common accent and dirty shoes – or preferably, no shoes at all.   *Lord Baden-Powell*

An extract from *Making Films for Pleasure and Profit* by Lord Baden-Powell (revised edition 1977)

The show was now really on the road. The Goodies had a producer, a director and bags of money. Actually Louie Bunce had the bags; and the money.

"Boys, there's no point in the readies rotting away in some silly old bank, much better it should be 'working' for me. What? Oh yes, and for you of course. Trust me, banks aren't safe, and I should know."

It was agreed that Graeme should take care of the technical side – cameras, lights etc – while Bill was investigating studios, costume, make-up and scenery. Tim was left in charge of casting as he had the hat, and the cleanest shoes.

The news that casting was going on soon spread like wildfire. Letters came pouring into the Goodies' office and Tim discovered that his headaches had only just begun. His desk was covered. Who was he going to disappoint?

Tim's Casting Notes

THE GOODIES FILM
Cast in order of importance

TIM.........................Tim Brooke-Taylor

GRAEME........................Graeme Garden

BILL...............Bill Oddie (For the time being)

A DOG...............To be Cast (Possibly as 'Bill')

A BAD PERSON......................To be Cast

A LOVABLE CHILD.................To be Cast

A WOMAN ....To be Cast

A CAST OF THOUSANDS ....To be Cast

om **OLIVER REED**

Dear Little-jumped-up-nobodies,
            I'm available, you'll
be delighted to hear, to start filming
on Monday and Keith says he can make
it too. We'll let you know where we're
going to be so you can bring the
cameras etc to us. I enclose a recent
photo of myself which you can pin
up in your office.
            Mine Sincerely,

Olly Reed.   x

*I told him what he
could do with himself.
It'll be anatomically
impressive if he
manages it.*

HENRY KISSINGER
'DUNROAMIN'
WASHINGTON AC

THE UNIGATE MILK CO

Dear Mr Taylor,   No doubt you are
at present wondering where to fi
milk at a reasonable price, an
essential, of course, for your ne
ilm?
            Your worries are at an
end and I enclose a recent photogra
of a versatile little Red Top.
            Yours Creamily,

M.T.Bottle.   *Yes* ✓

?

DUSTIN HOFFMANN

CALIFORNIA

*Dear Goodies,
I have been acting for several years
now. Maybe you will have heard of me.
I was in the "Graduate" "Midnight Cowboy"
and several other films. I have recently
made appearances in "the Two Ronnies" and
the "Benny Hill Show". I enclose a recent
photo of myself.
            Sincerely,   Never heard of
            Dustin Hoffmann   him*

Goodies,
            I enclose a recent picture of myself
e hope that you might be able to use me in
ew film.
            I haven't been quite so busy recent
ny wife wants me out of the house. I can s
v funny voice and stop wars if that's the
of thing you want.
            Yours

Henry Kissinger

x *Refused
Too long
in the
tooth —
and nose.*

At first I decided to concentrate on finding an actor to play the part of the villain. I tried the Yellow Pages, but there was nothing between Accumulator Manufacturers and Acupuncture Practitioners. There was nothing between Drains and Drapers for Drama either. Not wanting to waste the time that I'd already put in, I rang Forsythe's Drainaway 24 hr service. I asked for a quote for unblocking our drains and was told '£80 an hour'. I pointed out that not even a top paid television star would get that kind of money. He said he knew and that's why he'd given it up and gone into drains. But hadn't he done well. 'Good game, good game'. He tried to help though, by suggesting I bought a copy of *The Stage* where, apparently, a lot of actors advertise themselves.

DIRECTORY

IDA NADIR

A "BALLET" NUISANCE
c/o The Royal Ballet

DERMOT STAVEACRE
"THE SINGING BABOON"

STILL GOING STRONG

FRANK SINATRA

No Sole Agent

✶✶✶✶✶✶✶✶✶✶✶✶✶✶
✶ **melita** ✶
✶ ✶
✶ ✶ Fire Eater ✶
✶ ✶ Belly Dancer ✶
✶ ✶ Tassel Twirler ✶
✶ ✶ Chartered Surveyor ✶
✶✶✶✶✶✶✶✶✶✶✶✶✶✶

BOB MONKHOUSE
No Soul Agent

BOB MARLEY
Most *Pleasant*

THE New, New, New,
New, New, New, New,
New, New, New, New,
SEEKERS (re-forming)

Bruce Forsythe
"Singing in The Drain"
"Last Drain to San Fernando"
"Life is The Name of The Drain"
and other HITS

Barbie Cute contortionist
At present tied up in
Summer Season GT YARMOUTH

ROD McKUEN
and his amazing dog
PHAIDAUX

BABS AKIMBO
A THOUSAND AND ONE STUNTS
WITH A TRACTOR
AGRICULTURAL SHOWS AND
SYNODS

ENOCH POWELL
"THE CHOCOLATE
COLOURED COON"
South London
Barmitzvahs

Gypsy Rose Bygraves

stargazer extraordinaire
"One day Gypsy Rose B
will get a booking that
will make her employer very
rich and famous".

EDNA TOLE
"Naughty but nice"
STILL appearing as
President of Venezuela

DEREK & CLIVE
Children's parties

Martin Boorman
● "Now you see him,
● now you don't"

ROD STEWART
"Still one of the lads"
c/o The Noquestionsaskedgebundenbank, Zurich

Reginald Bosanquet

● *Balances a cat on his
head as he reads the news*
"Hair today, gone tomorrow"

FLORRIE BUNDER
Escapologist

No known address

Margaret Thatcher

Female Impersonator
"A BIT BLUE"

IVY BENSON
and her all girl band
with or without instruments

SYDNEY LOTTERBY
TV's Man of Mystery

THE New, New, New,
New, New, New, New
New, New, New, New
New, New, New, New
New, New, New, New
New, New, New, New
New, New, New, New
New, New, New, New
SEEKERS

NO CONNECTION WITH
THE New, New, New,
New, New, New, New,
New, New, New, New,
New, New, New, New,
New, New, New, New,
New, New, New, New,
SEEKERS
or
THE NEW SEEKERS
or
THE SEEKERS

HAROLD WILSON
Britain's foremost dialect comedian

Bob Hope

RUNNER UP
NEW FACES

THE BEATLES

Only dates available **July 1993**

"TWO EARS" LAYBELL
He is a "stereo" *type*

REGINALD BOSANQUET

Dear Mr Brooke-Taylor,
Thank you for your letter inviting me to be
in your film.
Here is the News.
Today fighting broke out in 43 Bridgenorth St
when my Irish cat jumped off my head and attacked
the man who had come to do the drains. Mr Forsyth
is then believed to have cried out 'Aaargh!',
done a quick tap dance, sung a couple of songs,
and smashed me in the teeth. An all round
entertainer now engaged in drainage work is
helping police with their enquiries.
This is Reginald Bosanquet,
News at Ten, Ruislip Hospital
Reggie
P.S. Sorry, can't make it
P.P.S. Is it really true the hat's been found?

It was a shame about Reggie Bosanquet. Mind you he'd have made a rotten villain, he's got far too nice a speaking voice and I don't think anyone's ever seen his shoes. Phaidaux, Rod McKuen's dog sounded just right for the dog lead so I rang his number. There was just a message on an Answering Machine.

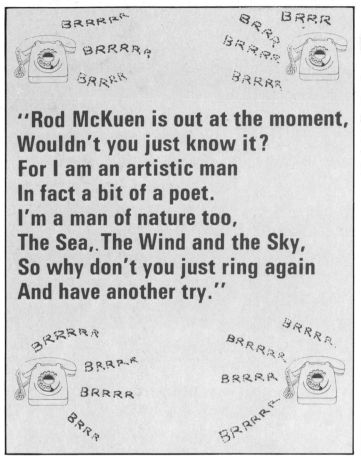

"Rod McKuen is out at the moment,
Wouldn't you just know it?
For I am an artistic man
In fact a bit of a poet.
I'm a man of nature too,
The Sea, The Wind and the Sky,
So why don't you just ring again
And have another try."

(Reprinted with the kind permission of the author and *Pretentious Publications Ltd.*)

I got hold of him in the end though. By the scruff of his neck actually, as I kicked him out of the house. Phaidaux was useless. He couldn't do a single trick and I don't think the carpet will ever be the same again. All the dogs I tried were useless – Lassie, Rin Tin Tin, Henry – none of them could do anything. Actually that's no quite true, Lassie could beg; and to be fair it was an impressive sight as she walked round the room on her hind legs with a white stick, dark glasses and tin mug. But that was all she could do. I told her we'd let her know and she bit me on the leg.

I then had a brainwave. At least it seemed a good idea at the time. We would cast a complete unknown! A dog eating in a downtown diner maybe, completely unaware, as I happened to glance across a crowded room, that stardom was just around the corner. I launched a campaign and the press coverage was absolutely fantastic.

Well I wasn't to know Crufts was on that week. In no time at all I was up to my ears in Shampoodles. Every shape, size and colour; they all came bounding round. I was licked, bitten, scratched – everything – and that was only the owners. Miserable breeders!
But I was 'saved' by Equity.

Equity
Stratford   =on=Avon
Canine division

Dear Sir,
      A Mr McKuen has brought to our notice that you are considering a non-union member for a part in your projected film. Only fully paid up Equity members (Canine section) can be employed.
So there!

Yours,
M. GORING

Marius Goring (stage name: Vanessa Redgrave.)

General secretary: **William Shakespeare**   Treasurer: **W. Shakespeare (Mrs.)**
Secretary to the General secretary: **Ann Hathaway**
Branch secretary (Cat division): **Tibbles Shakespeare**   Bone secretary (Canine division): **Fido Shakespeare**
Secretary (Gibbon division): **Funky Shakespeare**

Well that was that as far as I was concerned. What's a good, clean family film without a little honest mutt. To be truthful I wasn't too keen on our doggy friends at that moment and when, the next morning, a strangely shaped shihtzu called round I was all for giving it one of my famous banana kicks. But it spoke.
"We've brought you a letter, haven't we? Yes", it said.
I read the letter.

Please find, enclosed, a page from 'The Spotlight'.
Yours Faithfully,
Two Admirers."

And it was just signed with a couple of paw marks.

Please find, enclosed, a page from 'The Spotlight' Yours faithfully Two Admirers

ORSON WELLES

'VOICE OVER' FOR FINDUS FISH FINGERS
(also radio work)

C/O
INTERNATIONAL FAMOUS AGENCY
Palmers Green

KENNETH WROTTS

Recent TV:
Man in queue—Z CARS
Passer-by—THE BROTHERS
Man in corner—PLAY FOR TODAY
Cyclist—THE SWEENEY
Dead body—THE SURVIVORS
Man with back to camera—I CLAUDIUS
Man waving scarf—MATCH OF THE DAY
Silent onlooker—UPSTAIRS, DOWNSTAIRS
Man crossing road—NEWS AT TEN
Man looking out of window—SOFTLY SOFTLY
Title role—HAMLET
Man in pub—CORONATION STREET

C/o Mrs. K. Wrotts
FLAT 23,075
COLOSSUS DWELLINGS, E.14

CHENG FENG WONG

Recent TV:
Algy in THE IMPORTANCE OF BEING
EARNEST.
Lord Hemsley in UPSTAIRS DOWNSTAIRS.
On Stage:
The Dame—BABES IN THE WOOD

C/o Mrs. K. Wrott
FLAT 23,075
COLOSSUS DWELLINGS, E.14

THE YUGOSLAVIAN ARMY

Recent TV:
War and Peace—BBC
Playaway—BBC

C/o Bernard Tito
(Sole agents)
BELGRADE
YUGOSLAVIA

KURK DOUGLAS

Grumpy—SNOW WHITE AND THE SEVEN DWARFS *1971*
Sleepy—SNOW WHITE AND THE SEVEN DWARFS *1972*
Sneezy—SNOW WHITE AND THE SEVEN DWARFS *1973*
Happy—SNOW WHITE AND THE SEVEN DWARFS *1974*
Dopey—SNOW WHITE AND THE SEVEN DWARFS *1975*
Bashful—SNOW WHITE AND THE SEVEN DWARFS *1976*
Doc—GENERAL HOSPITAL *1977*

Sole Agent: Fellini
       ROMA 2

Eyes: Hazel   Size: Hazel Nuts

JON WAYNE

Title Role—GOLIATH*
The Giant—JACK AND THE BEANSTALK*
Title Role—KING KONG*
Title Role—KRAKATOA*
A Tooth—JAWS

Sole Agent: Fellini
       ROMA 2

Model shots only

BERT LANCASTER

Films:
"THE VERY YOUNG WINSTON"
"TOM BROWN'S NURSERY SCHOOLDAYS"
"KITTEN ON A HOT TIN ROOF"

TV:
As Jack Ford in "WHEN THE BOAT GOES OUT"

Rain Over Norfolk—WEATHER FORECAST
       BBC July 1976

Sole Agent: Fellini
       ROMA 2

CHARLTON HESTEN

Films include: "THE INVISIBLE MAN",
"THE LADY VANISHES", "THE RETURN
OF THE INVISIBLE MAN", "THE MAN
WHO NEVER WAS".   *Currently disappearing at:*
       The Playhouse,
       BUXTON

Sole Agent: Fellini Except as Nun Agent: Ken Russell

ROMA (1) 2   BOLOGNA (2) 3.

And that was how Jon Wayne and Bert Lancaster, both Equity members, got their first big break in films. They promised they'd be there for the first day of shooting with a well pressed dog skin and nice clean paws.

Spotlight was also invaluable for finding our cast of thousands.

Bernard Tito proved to be a friendly man, and promised that the Yugoslavian Army would be free on the given dates. Their present run at the Alhambra, Bradford, in *Des O'Connor Entertains*, where they play the part of the audience, would have ended by then and barring civil wars or invasions there was nothing to stop them appearing on time. He was also quite happy for all his men to be seen to be wearing a Windermere and Coniston Surgical Truss, indeed most of them would be able to provide their own. He thought it only fair to point out however that a Yugoslavian version of the song *We're tickled to death with our Trusses* would lose rather a lot in the translation.

But there still seemed to be something missing. It needed a few of those names which can make a film really rather special. A film like "White Christmas" for instance. I rang Hollywood for a cast list. It was a bad line but I managed to explain what I wanted and they very quickly and efficiently said 'Pardon'. After a time they managed to find what I was looking for as it was apparently written on their copy of the sheet music. I copied it down.

⋆ *White Christmas*

Theme Song / Words & Music

"Two Ears" Laybelle ?!

White Christmas - Cast Lis

Emma Dreaming
Arfur White
Chris Muss

Jess Like-Dee
Juan Swee
Hugh Sterno

Wendy Treetops-Glisse
Anne Chilled-Wren
Liz Anne
"Two Ears" Laybelle
Cindy Snow.

Emma Dreaming
Arfur White
Chris Musswit
Avery Crease
Miss Carr
Dai Wright.

Mayor Dazeby
Mary Anne Bright.

Anne-May Hall-York-Rhy
Mrs B. White

I was inundated with letters from agents recommending their clients – which often included people who hadn't appeared in films for years and years.

THE NEC

ole Representatives

Miriam Nesbi...

Glenn Miller

Buster Keaton

Sir Henry Irving

THE NECROFILMIC AGENCY

Specialists in people who haven't appeared in films for years and years.

Dear Mr Brooke-Taylor,

We hear you are at present casting the forthcoming Goodies movie. May we suggest that several of our clients may be suitable for your needs. Admittedly many of them may be rather decomposed, and indeed ALL of them are dead (this is guaranteed; doctor's certificate issued with every contract) but their names live on – and have enormous "drawing-power". Moreover, they are very little trouble to work with – no tantrums, walk outs etc. – and their fees are very reasonable.

There is absolutely NO DECEPTION involved – these great stars really can appear in YOUR film. All "remains" are guaranteed genuine. Indeed, many of them are still recognisable, and with the aid of a little make-up are certainly as vivacious as many of today's so-called film stars!

We enclose a list of clients and some recent photos. If there are any stars *1 you particularly want who are not on our list, we can usually obtain them, for a small extra "exhumation charge".

Yours
Berk 'n Her

BERK'N HER

(former speciality magic duo)

Notes
*1   All such stars requested MUST already be deceased. We are not prepared to kill living stars *2 (no matter how decrepit they may be)
*2   There are certain obvious exceptions to this rule: eg Oliver Reed, Vanessa Redgrave, Keith Moon etc. etc.

★

Mary Pickford

And Many More –
new names added every week!

Rudolf Valentino

...e Keystone Cops

...glas Fairbanks

Amos & Andy

Louie Bunce Productions Inc.

Dear Tim,
    I thought I'd relieve you of some of your casting chores. Yesterday, I interviewed Miss Hills. Wasn't <u>sure</u> if she was right for the part at first, but she thoroughly impressed me – twice. In fact she's impressing me again right now.
    Please excuse shaky handwriting, sincerely,

Louie

...en our producer lent a helping hand . . .

and a halt thousand

Cheeky Beverley Hills has certainly got a lot to beam about. For, this week, buxom Bev was told that she and two and a half thousand other girls might easily be considered for a part in the Goodies' new film.

"Goody, goody, yum yum," say we!

Bouncy Beverley doesn't believe in casting couches – the top of the filing cabinet'll do her! – and we should know! Whoops!

She has a close friendship with producer Louie Bunce, "but I hope he won't hold it against me!" Whoops again! "Words aren't my strong points," adds Bev modestly, "and be honest, I'm a lousy actress – but I do go like the clappers!" Somehow she makes everything sound naughty!

Yes, Callipygian Beverley's certainly got the Goodies for the Goodies, but she's not just a pretty face – she's got brains too! She feels that the minimum lending rate has nothing to do with her,

and that marriage and having children is something that she's never thought about.

Bubbly Beverley has something to say about Women's Libbers too: "What about the men and the trouble they have with *their* libbers?"

Showbiz may be a gamble but we wouldn't mind putting a few bob on this young filly. As they say, well, we do anyway: "There's gold in them thar Hills!"

and now to find a child star . . .

Spring Selection

Promising Three Year Olds all ready for use now . . .

MANDY

Charming doll-like child. Matured in cellar for three years. She blinks. Could make your mechanical walking doll appear amazing in suitable commercial. Cries and wets herself if required.

SAMANTHA

The famous O'Grady all-girl quads (only two pictured here). Get round the ridiculous child labour laws with these 4 Samanthas. They work 6 hour shifts.

24 hour service: Commercials made and Chimneys swept.

NOSHER (no picture)

Good appetite. Nosher will eat anything, even *your* product. With coaxing will throw up Brand X.

Accents: Posh, Common and Foreign. Bred from our own stock.

Father is Nobel Peace Prize Winner. Mother—All-in mud wrestler.

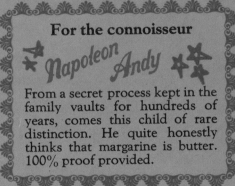

For the connoisseur

Napoleon Andy

From a secret process kept in the family vaults for hundreds of years, comes this child of rare distinction. He quite honestly thinks that margarine is butter. 100% proof provided.

BARABBAS (no picture)

From same unique strain as above. Barabbas is ideal for Public Service films.

Guaranteed to: Chase ball under traffic, trip down badly lit stairs, pour pan of boiling oil on himself, pick your wallet.

Previous experience: a rather nasty one behind the bus shelter.

Good with animals.

Several convictions. Age 3 – could pass for 18.

STUNT CHILDREN

We have a small selection of children from 2 - 7 years old. Some colours discontinued.

They can all: fall from ten storey buildings, jump fourteen buses on motor bikes, go over Niagara Falls in a barrel, climb Everest, put their head in a lion's mouth, look dead under water.

Only one "take" guaranteed.

STOP PRESS

Coming soon
HEINZ

```
Careful breeding
has produced this
Caucasian-negro-
oriental-fully
authenticated
red indian.
```

April delivery

SMUGSY

Highly versatile performer. Smugsy can play tough, beefburger, dirty-football shirt type *or* butter-wouldn't melt-in-the-mouth choirboy. Pictured above in two recent roles for Pears Soap. Bred i[n] England, and trained in Ireland wit[h] American owner.

Tim had every reason to feel pleased as he gazed lovingly at the twin reflections of himself in his nice shiny shoes. Admittedly he hadn't found a 'bad person' yet but, if the worst came to the worst, the character of 'Bill' could always double for that. He had cleverly defused a potentially explosive situation by casting Rita Acapulco *and* Beverley Hills as 'the Woman'; and he felt confident that Bonzo the Wonder Dog played by a double-dwarved Shihtzu would become a part of motion picture history. With the birth of Heinz, the Lovable Child, timed exactly for the first day of shooting and, with the promise of the entire Yugoslavian Army, his job was completed. The film was now cast. The rest was up to Bill and Graeme.

Graeme knew what he wanted . . . now he had to get it!

CHAPTER SIX
TECHNICAL EQUIPMENT

I must confess I can never look upon a 16mm Arriflex, a Bell and Howell 636, or even a Beaulieu 4008 Z MC Schneider Macro 11-11.8 Zoom Lens without being instantly put in mind of the tale of the foolish tribesman and the wise cameraman.

The story is told – by me anyway – how, many years ago, in a wild and distant land – let us call it Bingo Bongo Land – there dwelt an undiscovered tribe of dark skinned folk – let us call them the Golly Mop tribe – whose leader was a rough fellow, whom we shall call Jumby Lumby (though his real name was Cardew). The Golly Mops lived in the hot jungle and wore no neckerchieves, neither did they have nicely shined shoes. They had never set eyes on a white man; and little could they know that the day would soon come when they, like all undiscovered tribes before them, would be visited by the camera team of *The World About Us* (BBC 2 7.30 on Sundays).

Well, inevitably, the day did come. But when Jumby Lumby beheld the dedicated little BBC team of a director, two camera operators, three assistants, two continuity girls, eight 'sparks', four catering, three make-up, nineteen costume, the director's 'friend' and two lorry loads of photographic equipment (plus a second unit that was filming the first unit for a *Horizon* feature on the making of *The World About Us* . . . not forgetting the team from *Blue Peter* who were filming the second unit for an item on *The making of a BBC documentary* . . . and of course, the team from *Man Alive*, who were hoping to nick a few ideas . . . oh and also three

researchers from *This is Your Life* who were recording a personal message from the tea lady who was distantly related to Nicholas Parsons, he rolled his eyes.

Jumby Lumby was confused and perplexed, and so were all the Golly Mops; so much so that they let down the continuity girls and raped the lorries' tyres. They also desembowelled the costumes, ate the make up, insulted the director by shrinking his head, set fire to the director's 'friend', and commiserated with the tea lady.

Now, many would have considered the behaviour of Jumby Lumby and his friends to be thoroughly unsporting. However, there was amongst the BBC team a wise cameraman.

He reasoned with himself, thinking; "Though these people are behaving impolitely, yet are they uncivilized and not yet tutored in the ways of gentlemen. There is no point in calling them 'unsporting' . . . I must reason with them and persuade them to forsake their unruliness, otherwise I'm liable to get my goolies chopped off. I see that they are in the habit of wearing a bunch of beads dangling from their belts . . . at least, I hope they are beads . . . perhaps they would care to trade."

Whereupon, the wise cameraman pointed admiringly at Jumby Lumby's beads (hoping they were beads), and, using the only language he could – English – he enquired if Jumby Lumby would be willing to barter with them. Jumby Lumby nodded his agreement and indicated that he wished to know what the wise cameraman would give him in return.

Now, as luck would have it, the wise cameraman had in his

a bright new penny, a piece of chewing gum and a stone. Each was refused, and ended up respectively in the wise cameraman's right nostril, his leaft ear-hole, and another place.

The wise cameraman was in despair as to know what could possibly please Jumby Lumby when suddenly Jumby Lumby indicated that he *would* be willing to exchange his beads for a 16mm Arriflex, a Bell and Howell 636, a Beaulieu 4008 Z MC Schneider Macro 11-11.8 Zoom Lens, and the rest of the gear. And so the deal was done. The wise cameraman had a cluster of beads (at least he hoped they *were* beads) and Jumby Lumby had eleven thousand quids worth of cine equipment. An uneven exchange you might well think. And yet, I ask you: "who got the better of the bargain?" The wise cameraman returned to England's green and pleasant land, and became a wise bead seller (well his customers think they're beads) and now has a nice little stall down the Portobello Road; whilst Jumby Lumby, we can be sure, is still stuck in the nasty hot jungle, with a load of gear, that to him, is totally worthless.

Lord Baden-Powell

pocket a small pen knife with an attachment for taking stones out of horses' hooves, and incorporating a camel hair brush for polishing shoes. This he duly produced and offered it to Jumby Lumby. Whereupon Jumby Lumby smiled, took the implement twixt his forefinger and thumb, and stuffed it up the wise cameraman's left nostril. Next, the wise cameraman, fearing lest his offer had insulted Jumby Lumby, offered him

An extract from Making Films for Pleasure and Profit by Lord Baden-Powell

Gathering the Bumph

So Graeme set to his task of assembling all the equipment necessary to the making of a great Motion Picture . . . or a rotten one, come to think of it. Painstakingly he researched through all the available literature. He pored over the pile of magazines in the loo; then dried them off, and read them. And he spent two weeks in *Sid's Book Mart* diligently searching through reams of irritatingly irrelevant smut in the hope of winkling out a few smidgeons of technical information.

As you probably know we are one of
Sweden's largest producers of
...graphy. specializing in
...the past we have
...omers direct

IMPORTANT
ANNOUNCEMENT
...OULTON IM...

FILM SCENE CURRENT...

cinema

FILMS ILLUSTRATED

E MAGAZINE THAT LOVES MOVIES

Wil...
The comic for...

How to make a
camera out of
matchboxes...

How to batter
your granny

A study of
symbolism
in Bertolucci's
later films...

55p/ $2.00

bfi

INTERNATIONAL ...ARTERLY

SIGH... SOU...

Also in this ISSUE...

Portable HiFi,
Automatic washing machines,
Automatic HiFi,
Automatic Portable
washing machines
Lens Caps,
Non-Automatic non-portable H
(with built-in washing machines)
Contraceptives (with built-in HiF
but without washing machines)

Which?

BLOBS

ARE THEY REALLY A RELIABLE WAY TO JUDGE THE QUALITY OF CONSUMER GOODS?

EXCH... & M...

Leisure

● **Arts & Crafts**
Aardvark polishing, Artificial
limb carving, balls, cadavers,
cardiac respirators, camp
little nonsenses, choreographers
woolly tights, cheap things,
Clergyman's chromium plated
earplugs, Coniston &
Windermere
surgical trusses & appliances,

● **Music**
Saxaphones, saxipl...
session musicians
string synthesizer
synthesizer synth...
sylophones, Xyle...
Zylophones.
● Photogra...
Apertures...
...e cameras...

march 19...

film... and...

* REQUIRES
FURTHER INVESTIGAT...
Dr. G.

...ENS...

...RI...

43 TEENA...
...ory in words an...
...n Private. Co...
...climax shots.
...the enc...

PLUS FREE

SOCAN

BLUE

Kin
dren...

Non Artistic movie maker Aug 77

ARTISTIC MOVIE MAKER

Produced by Jodrell Press

Only 30p CINEMA
Not for sale to persons under 18 years of age. Vol. 8 No. 12

The daily grind goes on

CONTINENTAL
EFLECTING TODAY'S CINEMA   KNOW WHAT WE ME

ADVERTISEMENT

USED BY PRIMITIVE
TRIBES THE
WORLD
OVER ...

photographic
equipment from
JUMBY-LUMBY
MAIL ORDER SERVICE

CARDEW SAYS ...
We Golly-Mops spend hours doing
ourselves up in ostrich feathers, sticking
bones through our noses and making up
silly rituals – so we're simply not going to
put up with fuzzy-focus & bad framing.
We *know* a good camera when we're shot
by one, and thats why we stock ONLY
THE BEST!

Screens made
from REAL
Missionary
skin

The Black
Sound of
Music

Giraffe
quadro-
pod

us
essories
used in
e jungle
housands
years ...

AVAILABLE NOW
"JUMBY -LUMBY'
FILMS.

Special 25% discount ONLY to
Documentary Directors holding a BBC
Club Card.

EW TITLES ~ this season

TEREST
TRAVEL

VENTURE

EX

USIC &
OMEDY

"28 Tribal Dances" – Gazelle dance, head
shrinking dance, gay gordons,
etc., Six Undiscovered
Tribes – All Different ...
"Schweitzers Last Stand"
With a host of "jungle
stars" including Martin
Boorman, Lord Lucan &
the *original* Glenn Miller
Orchestra.
Plus – "Confessions of a
Distant Relative of
Nicholas Parsons – Up
the Jungle" (6 reels)

3 REEL
FEATURETTES

Also from
'Jumby-Lumby'
Beads, dried
goolies, make-
p girls etc.

AMAZING OFFER!
With every 3 films you buy, we will send you
Jeffrey Boswell, or David Attenborough
– *Entirely free!!!*

MBY

Call Amazonia 3511 – for more info

AMAZING
VALUE

Saturday 17th DAILY MIRROR

ex-army
GERMAN
CAMERAS

LINTZ
Mk II

★ 23 speeds
★ 200m Lens
   x 503 magnification.
★ Macro attachment – focusses
   down to 2 millimetres.
★ Plus features available only on
   Cameras costing at least six
   million pounds ...
This truly incredible camera
given away FREE to anyone
who writes to box 35

INSIDE: Gore Vidal's Caligula-Macho-Emmanuelle

FILM REVIEW

(Extract from Minutes Book)

SPECIAL FINANCIAL MEETING OF THE GOODIES FILM-MAKING COMMITTEE.

Subject: Purchase of Film Making equipment.

Dr Garden presented his list of projected purchases, which was accepted by the committee, with the following amendations:

a) **Delete** 'three dozen shrunken heads, a brace of make-up girls and a hippo'

b) **Delete** 'Amanda' . . . the Inflatable Bed Mate'

c) **Delete** 'Twenty years subscription to 'Tax Evaders Which'.

d) **Delete** 'Four pairs of x 1000 Ex Army German Binoculars, six water beds, fourteen foam rubber cubes and twelve pairs of nature shoes.

e) **Add** 'A cine Camera'.

Mr Garden then proposed the motions that

a) He should now be allowed to go shopping

b) He should be given the money with which to do so.

The Motions were put to the vote, a 'quorum' being present consisting of Mr Oddie (who was acting treasurer . . . and acting awfully well too, Tim please note.) (Mr Brooke Taylor was absent, casting; whilst Mr Garden was ineligible to vote as he was the subject of the Motion).

The first motion (That Mr Garden could go shopping) was carried by a small majority (Mr Oddie).

The second motion (that he should have any money) was defeated unanimously. Mr Oddie was then carried, by Mr Garden, and dropped on the fire.

Mr Garden then pointed out that the fact that he was to be allowed no money was irrelevant, since we didn't *have* any money, since all funds had been transferred to the safe-keeping of Mr Louis Bunce.

It was finally agreed to write to Mr Louis Bunce to request the release of certain monies for the purchase of photographic equipment.

His reply follows . . .

> *The Delfont Wing*
> *Pinewood Debtors Prison (For Bankrupt Film Producers)*
>
> *RE: Requested release of certain monies.*
>
> *Dear Lads,*
> *Don't let the temporary address worry you. Your money is safe in cigars, Rolls Royces, and the lining of my left trouser leg. Alas, no monies – certain or uncertain – can be released, until I am!*
> *However, tell you what . . . if you pay it out of your own pocket for the moment, we will consider it to be in lieu of production royalties that I would eventually receive, which I will, however, in this instance, loan you in advance – subject of course to the normal sliding scale of interest applicable in these cases to such a loan and relating in the usual way to the index of inflation.*
> *And you can pay me back when I get out. O.K.?*
> *Done! (yet again!!!)*
> *Happy shopping and don't bother to thank me.*
>
> Louie
> sincerely
>
>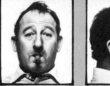
>
> *NUMBER: 32588 12 900 36*
> *(BUT, to YOU . . . 300)*

Clearly, Graeme had a problem. However, as it turned out, he *did* have a camera – a perfectly good 16mm Bolex, which he'd been given for his third birthday, but had soon grown tired of and chucked it in the attic, along with the three dimensional chess set and the *Let's Play Blood Donors* game.

But Graeme wanted accessories: lenses, tripods, filters, and so on. The fact was, he had no money, but, to an economic genius, and a born loony, the dilemma was not insurmountable.

ACCOUNTS FOR PURCHASE OF TECHNICAL EQUIPMENT

INCOME:	
Sale of Bolex Camera:	£544.13½p
OUTGO:	
Nikkormat Fifteen Foot Lens	£478.00
"Garbolegs" Tripod	35.05
Packet of Filters	15.02
Hire of lorry to carry lens home in	15.54
Materials to make Camera:	
Four boxes of matches	0.08
Glue	0.34½
Button	0.01½
Total Cost:	£544.15p

15½
−13½
= 1½P !

oh crikey—that's torn it.

Sorry!

Disaster

But even a genius can make a slip up . . . the disastrous fact was that they were already one and a half pence over budget! The film was in jeopardy even before it had begun.

Disaster averted

But fortune favours the bold (and the loony). Even as Graeme resolved himself to having to make do with a *three* match-box camera, the glad news came that they had been awarded an Arts Council Grant, which almost covered the debt.

Then, in the same issue of *Time Out*, they read that Louis Bunce had been awarded a Knighthood for his services to the British economy. He was immediately released from debtors prison for fear the Queen should look a bit of a nana. And as a gesture of good faith, he offered to make up the extra half penny, in return for a further six and a half per cent Royalty.

The Goodies were back on course. It remained only to hire a first rate camera crew. With a fifteen foot zoom lens to handle, they needed to be something special, and lucky it was that Bill happened to tune in for *Match of the Day* only to find that it had been put back in favour of *The Edinburgh Photographic Tattoo*.

No. 1 Crew

Fastest Crew at
Edinburgh Photographic Tattoo
'74, '75, and '77

QUEEN'S OWN ARMOURED PHOTOGRAPHERS

* They can strip a Brownie in 25 seconds
* Amazing 'light show' – 150 flashes in perfect unison!
* Spectacular Musical Clapper-board Routine

WEDDINGS, NUDIE PICS, BABY PORTRAITS, FEATURE FILMS ETC.
Bookings being taken for Autumn 1977

A begging letter from Tim, and a blackmail note from Louis, and they were booked.

Meanwhile, Bill was getting into costumes.

CHAPTER SEVEN
COSTUME AND MAKE UP

You can always tell a man's character by looking at his shoes. A self-conscious person will say "oi, stop looking at my shoes". Otherwise, these rules apply: Nice clean shoes – nice clean character. Dirty shoes – dirty mind. High heels – which brings me on to make-up. Personally I favour just a touch of rouge and a smudge of mascara to set-off my woggle.*

Lord Baden-Powell

*Recommended further reading: 'Beauty hints for Boys' Lord B-P. '75.

An extract from Making Films for Pleasure and Profit by Lord Baden-Powell

On April 21st, Bill was duly given a prospective cast list and, blissfully oblivious of the changes that were to come, he began assembling the wardrobe.

Letter to Nathmans,
Theatrical Costumiers, Old Queen St., W.C.

From: Maison de Little Willie
(Wardrobe designer to The Goodies)
Has own chisel and nails.

Dear Nathi poos,
    Please supply cozzies for the following;
A lovable child. A bad person. A woman. A cast of thousands. Timbo, Graybags, and me. Sorry I can't give you more details. Just feel free . . . as if I have to tell YOU that! Which reminds me, I hope the wrist is better.
Ta.

Love

Little Willie

Oh P.S. Better chuck in a nice butch dog-skin. Jon and Bert say they've got their own, but you know what these midgets go for – so camp! They'll probably come done up as a poncy little Shihtzu or something.

Reply from Nathmans Theatrical Costumiers: Costumes Hired . . . and lowered

Dear Little Willie,
    Which reminds me, the wrist is better.
Bit low on dog skins at the moment – Rock version of The Lady and the Tramp *at the Young Vic next week, but I can let you have a six legged Pantomime dromedary. Hope you can work round it.*
Also find cozzies enclosed as following.
Lovable child (no such thing, dear!) : one nappy (sorry about the stains, the cat had conjunctivitis)
A woman: One nuns habit (Keep Ken happy eh?)
A bad person: David Kossof's smoking jacket (bad enough for you?)
The Goodies: Oh perish the impertinence, sugardrawers! You know what you look good in better than me. Whatever you feel comfy in. Mind you, I hope Tim's not going to wear that awful hat.
Cast of thousands: Hardly specific are you, love?!
Anyway, we've just had the returns from Salome and The Desert Song . . . so . . . 36 pairs of see-through pantaloons, 36 tin foil bras, 35 yashmaks (always a bold one isn't there?) and 254 veils (7 each and a couple of spares) O.K.?
Break a leg.

Love

Nathe

Bill was delighted with the way things were going. A few hitches perhaps, but nothing that couldn't be ironed out, or taken in. Everything seemed clear cut until . . .

THE WEEDS ARE ROOTED OUT

ON THE 24th of APRIL the Euphoria of the Goodies was cruelly shattered. Two small items in Variety, the American 'Bible of Showbiz', was to turn their innocent dreams into a living nightmare . . .

FILMS   RADIO   MUSIC

VARIETY

Published Weekly at 154 West 46th Street, New York, N.Y. 10036, by Variety, Inc. Annual subscription, $30. Single copies, 75 cents.
Second Class Postage Paid at New York, N.Y. and at Additional Mailing Offices
© COPYRIGHT, 1977, BY VARIETY, INC., ALL RIGHTS RESERVED

New York, Wednesday

NE
Seco

34205

UN MASTIC : TO RUT CINEMA

Feb. 1.
...a on in
...after
...civil
...some
...tion
...rut.
...with
...as
...ge
...ut
...s
.../

BUNCE NIXES 'GOODIES' PREEM AUG. PLUMP PLUGOLA.**

Sock surprise, top Production Veep of Louie Bunce Productions Inc, Louie Bunce, K.O.'s Brit T.V. Starskys: Tim Brown Tubing, Bile Oddie and Groan Garden from own film. Bunce goes for Marquee Boffo Billstars: ...ack Nicholson, James Caan, ...harles Bronson, Donald Suther-...nd, Elliott Gould, Michael ...rk, Lord Lucan, Roger Moore, ...l Newman, Sean Connery, ...bert Redford, Steve McQueen ...to play the part of "Tim". ...pectacled Greek thrush Nana ...skouri as "Graeme". Bolshoi ...t plotted for "Bill". ...Sci-Fi, Horror, Comedy, ...Disaster, Family Bonanza ...Preemed August after ...breaking 1 Billion Dolla...

Russell To Helm Swell Cellular Kidvid Boffo *

London April 24th
Ken Russell director of Sock-top-pop-rockera "Tommy" and other musoporn pix, plans indie feature rolling July. Film Players already slated: Oliver Reed, Keith Moon and Henry Kissinger as "the Goodies". Projected title: 'The Confessions of Banatti, Midget Nunnworshipper.'

Continued page 199

Wolper Tied To Haley Comet Via A 'Roots' S...

For a mere $4000, cash in advance, you can send for a complete translation of this week's 'Variety'.

SAMPLE TRANSLATION

*Roughly: Ken Russell is to direct a film version of a successful Television show that happens to appeal to children as well as adults.

**Louie Bunce has sacked the Goodies from their film. There is to be a premiere of the film in August. A lot of money will be spent on publicity so, if you happen to be someone who books films for cinemas, you are on to a good thing even if the film isn't all that good, due to excessive money used for publicity.

Feds Eye ... Not For P... But Anti-

Los Angeles,
Speculation that a netwo...
subsidiary may be a prim...
broke the otherwise tight-li...
dustry reaction to the sw...
Federal grand jury inves...
by areas as Amman, Cypr...
the Gulf, business during 197...
than doubled.)
One theatre owner even be...
the audiences have change...
"we've acquired a new clien...
particularly among the young...
another believes this is beca...
audiences have become displa...
forced to frequent situations in...
them, strange parts ...
cause ...

much more business ...
profitable ...

LETTER FROM

TIM BROOKE TAYLOR (CASTING DIRECTOR) TO LITTLE WILLIE...(COSTUME DESIGNER)

Dear Little Willie ,

You know I sent you a cast list the other day? And you know you've ordered lots of costumes? And you know you've spent hours designing the rest? And you know you thought you'd finished?
......

Well, you haven't.

First the good news -The Goodies are still in it.

Now the bad news - ~~you and Graeme aren't~~ we're not

I enclose a new cast list. Sorry if it messes you up a bit, but I know you'll work something out.   Love

Timbo

P.S. Its not ALL a cock up... at least THE DOG is DEFINITELY IN.

P.P.S.   In case you've forgotten.. dont forget:

NO CAMELS.
NO BELLY DANCERS
LOTS OF WINDERMERE AND CONISTON TRUSSES AND SURGICAL APPLIANCES.
GIVE PEPSI AND COKE A PLUG

MY HAT

P.P.P.S :   I agree with ~~Baden Powell~~ B-P about the shoes.

P.P.P.P.S: About the casting -nothing is really certain yet.

TIM: Jack Nicholson, James Caan, Charles Bronson, Donald Sutherland,
    Elliot Gould, Roger Moore, Michael York, Henry Kissinger???
                    On second thoughts, Tim Brooke Taylor - me!
BILL: The Bolshoi Ballet, Keith Moon?
GRAEME: Nana Mouskouri, or/and Oliver Reed?
CAST OF THOUSANDS: The Yugoslavian Army. DOG: Jon Wayne, Bert Lancaster.
A WOMAN: Rita Acapulco, Beverly Hills.......

LETTER FROM: LITTLE WILLIE
TO: TIM BROOKE TAYLOR (CASTING)

Dear Tim,

    Come off it!
What do they think I am? - a bleedin' fairy Godmother!
They'll get what they're given!

    Grrrrrrrrrr,

        Little Willie...

P.S. I enclose portfolio of some designs so far...
Oh gosh, I hope they like them.......

KEY to Costume for...

1 Jack Nicholson
2 James Caan
3 Donald Sutherland
4 Elliott Gould
5 Michael York
6 Roger Moore
7 Paul Newman
8 Sean Connery
9 Robert Redford
10 Steve MacQueen
11 Charles Bronson

to play

"Tim"* Costume for...
"Tim" - The 6 legged
Dromedary...
(stand-in for
Bonzo the Wonder Dog).

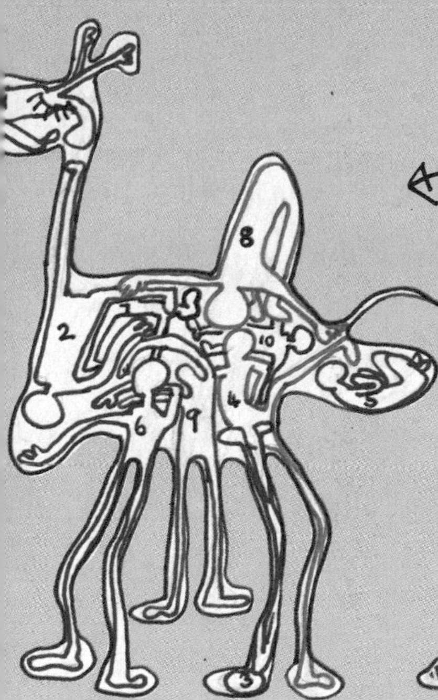

I realize he may not be happy with this casting -
but, sorry, we have a skin-ful!

Hat on Hire from "B-P Modes" Inc.
- optional - might hide wig?
Good or bad?

Costume for
Yugoslavian Army
(to play "Cast of thousands").

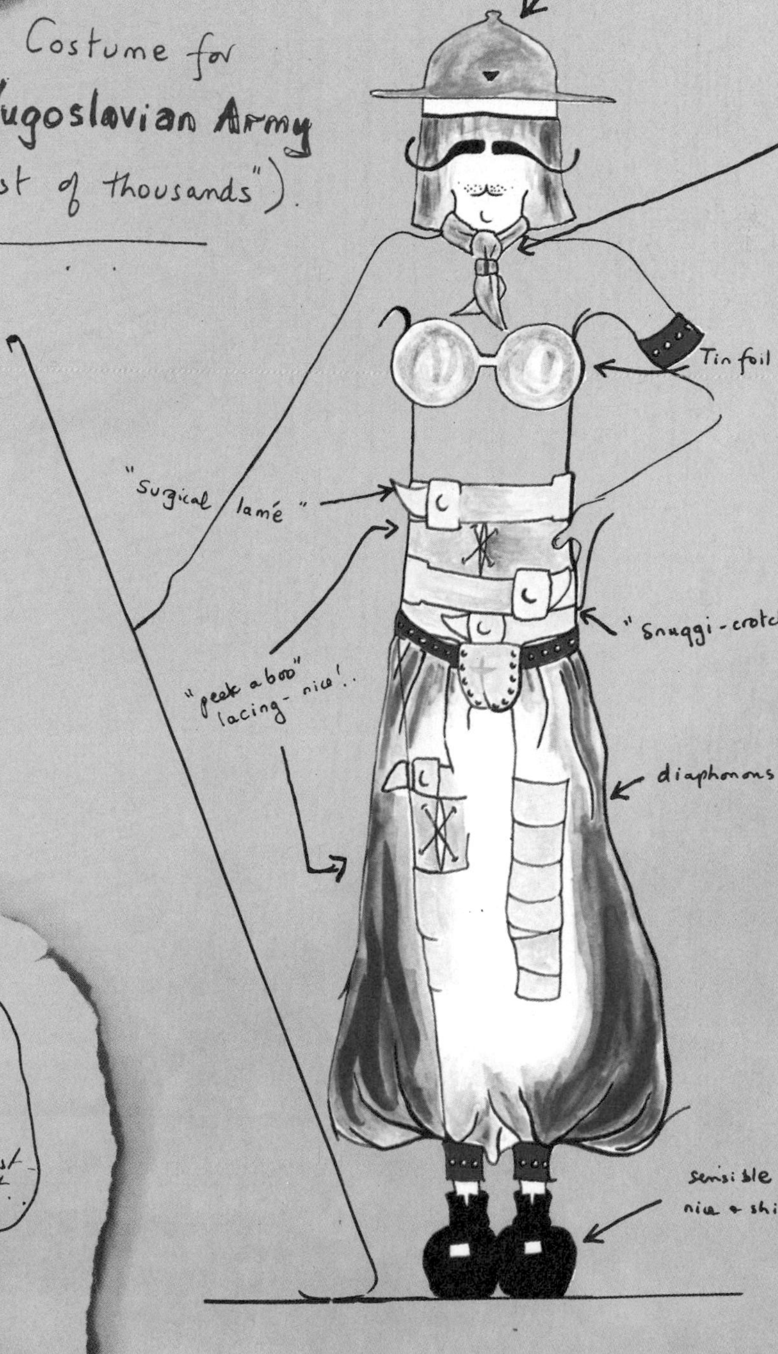

pretty woggle..

Tin foil (memo - Tim to
rescue off
Sunday Joint).

"Surgical lamé"

"Snuggi-crotch" military support.
by wind & con ltd.

"peek a boo"
lacing - nice!.

diaphanous - "Cling-film"?

* n.b. the part of
"Tim Brooke-Taylor" to be
played by Himself - don't
forget to bring own Union-Jack Waist-
coat.

* TIM'S HAT

sensible walking boots..
nice & shiny..

KEEP YOUR HAIR ON – CHUM!

A WORD OF ADVICE FROM THE HOUSE OF WOTWIG ©

Suppliers of toupees, hair arrangements, and discreet pate screening aids for the under-achiever in the well-clad scalp department, if you follow our meaning.
By appointment (but we're not allowed to say to whom. . .)

Absolutely confidential and reliable.

WOTWIG. ©
THE • NAME • YOU • CAN • TRUST

Age 25

Age 35

Today!

HUGH STERNO IS A VIOLINIST WITH THE L.S.O. HE USED TO BE BALD. . . BUT OH BOY LOOK AT HIM NOW! WHAT'S THAT ON HIS HEAD???!!!!!

IS IT A TOM-CAT? IS IT A DOOR-MAT?
IS IT A FUR-HAT? **NO!! IT'S A WIG !!**

YES, WE AT WOTWIG HAVE PLENTY TO SMILE ABOUT!

WOTWIG Board of Directors

Yes, more and more people throughout the world are astonishing their families and friends, thanks to WOTWIG!

IF YOUR HAIR'S RECEDING, THINNING, OR COMING OUT IN HANDFULS – INVEST IN A WOTWIG!

You'll soon notice the change, and so will everyone else! But they'll never believe it's a wig! TAKE IT OFF AND SHAKE IT IN THEIR FACES, AND THEY'LL STILL SAY IT CAN'T BE A WIG!!!

FOLLICLES!

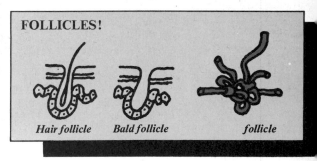

Hair follicle   *Bald follicle*   *follicle*

So don't be slow – cut out the coupon and send it off today.

I am interested in a WOTWIG fitting.
The colour of my hair is a) Ginger
                     b) Gingerish
                     c) Absent
Rush me one HIRSUTE CREATION to AUGMENT my COIFFURE!!

Signed.....................................
(I am over six years of age.)

NO OBLIGATION!
Send no money now! Send it first thing tomorrow morning to WOTWIG
℅ Frightfully Decent Good Old British Loan Co. . . . or else!

FOR A HEAD THAT REALLY STANDS OUT IN A CROWD – GET A WOTWIG!

ANNOUNCEMENT:
WOTWIG (Ltd) Cosmetic Scalp Furnishers and Wig Enforcement Agency has absolutely no connection with WOTWIG (Ltd) Deceased Ginger Hamster Importers.

NATURAL COLOUR!
Natural Human Hair comes in all shades of colour, from jet black to silver grey, from auburn to blond. Nature knows the importance of variety – and that's why WOTWIGS come in every possible shade of GINGER.

IF IT ISN'T GINGER, IT ISN'T A WOTW
Ask any experienced wig-sporter! The rich mellow tones of a genuine ginger wig seem to radiate a warmth that sets the sca aglow. Indeed it is often said that the only difference between WOTWIG wearer and a bald man with chunky marmalade smeared all over his pate is that the shrewd WOTWIG patron is seldom called "old marmalade bonce!" Or at least, not mo than once a day. If he stays in bed. With the light out.

WHY NOT PUT IT TO THE TEST?
Just go up to ANYONE with a handsome mop of ginger thatc and ask them:
"Where did you get that wig?"
Would you believe that 9 times out of 10 they'll answer:
"WOTWIG"?

CHAPTER EIGHT
LOCATIONS

Making a feature film is an excellent opportunity for getting out into the countryside: tracking, bird-spotting, woodcraft etc etc.   *Lord Baden-Powell*

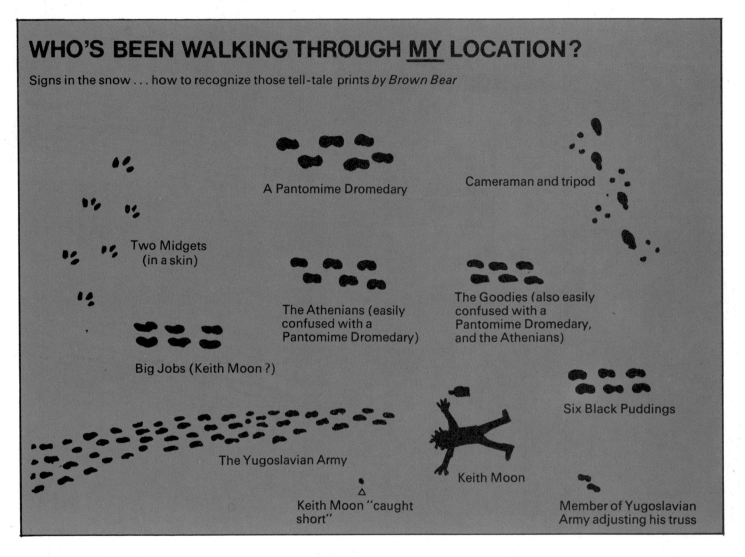

WHO'S BEEN WALKING THROUGH <u>MY</u> LOCATION?

Signs in the snow . . . how to recognize those tell-tale prints *by Brown Bear*

Two Midgets (in a skin)

A Pantomime Dromedary

Cameraman and tripod

Big Jobs (Keith Moon?)

The Athenians (easily confused with a Pantomime Dromedary)

The Goodies (also easily confused with a Pantomime Dromedary, and the Athenians)

Six Black Puddings

The Yugoslavian Army

Keith Moon

Keith Moon "caught short"

Member of Yugoslavian Army adjusting his truss

The choice of Locations was also Bill's responsibility, though 'Responsibility' is not a word normally associated with him. In the light of B-P's comment however, Bill was perhaps well suited to the job, since he had seen over three hundred species of birds in the British Isles alone (well, nobody's going to go with him are they?) In fact Tim and Graeme rather hoped that if they could get him to keep going off chasing birds, they might be able to keep him out of the film. Anyway, he applied himself to his new task with typical enthusiasm and lack of common sense.

Bill's rules to be borne in mind considering choice of locations for filming:

1: Try not to waste too much time travelling from one place to another. Locations should all be in the same area if possible.

2: Make maximum use of daylight hours.

3: Make sure there is a prolific supply of **Milk** . . . **Everyone** drinks **Milk** on **location** and **nothing else!**

4: Check out the bird spots.

5: Try to fit in a visit to Tim's granny in New Zealand.

Of course you are going to be pretty lucky to come up with a set of locations that fulfill all five requirements. Not surprisingly one of them had to go by the board. Bill decided that number one was least important and accordingly worked out the first couple of weeks schedule as follows.

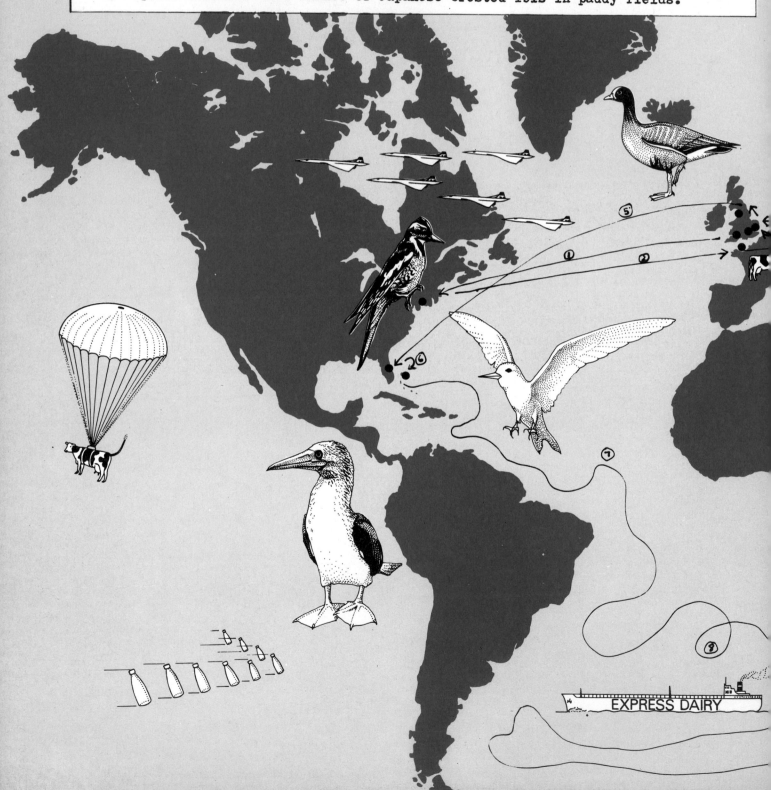

Suggested schedule for Goodies Film - Bill Oddie

<u>Day 1</u>: Unit pick up 14 crates of Gold Top from Cricklewood Deli. Travel to Slimbridge Wildfowl Trust. Excellent for rural scenes (we can 'shoot round' the wildfowl) (Check up identification features of Ring Necked Duck and look for Lesser Whitefront on The Dumbles)

<u>Day 1 (evening)</u>:Unit travels to New York (concorde) arrive so it's still light.

<u>Day 2</u>: Shoot street scenes and look for Yellow Bellied Sapsucker in Central Park. Milk from 'Hymie's Take Away' (5th and 43rd). Unit fly to Jersey.

<u>Day 3</u>:(still daylight owing to Time Zone difference) Unit visit St Brelaides Dairy for fresh Jersey milk. Hope to tick off Cettish Warbler in little marsh near beach huts. Fly to Japan.

<u>Day 4</u>: Arrive Tokyo (still daylight) Good for Kung Fu sequence? Milk supplied by Express Dairlee. Good chance of Japanese Crested Ibis in paddy fields.

EXPRESS DAIRY

Unit returns to England.
Day 5: Arrive Lake District (dawn). Goodwill visit to Windermere and Coniston Truss and Surgical Appliance Factory and overhaul trusses and appliances if neccesary. Visit Lake District's only pair of breeding Golden Eagles. Good area for mountain shots (Wuthering Heights etc.) Goats milk from Buttermere Farm. Unit leave for Florida.
Day 6: A.M. To rediscover Ivory Billed Woodpecker (extinct?)
       P.M. Morale-boosting pleasure trip to Bahamas (Bahama Bananaquit, Blue Faced Booby, Fairy Terns and Cocoanut Milk).
Days 7,8,9 and 10: Unit boards ship.
On board ship. (ship sequences?) If neccesary, 'mask out' the sea and shoot 'wet for dry'. Milk delivered by United Dairies helicopter. Look out for Yellow nosed Albatross and White vented Petrel.
Day 11: Unit dock at Auckland. Tim's granny and Lesser Spotted Kiwi.
Unit return to R.S.P.B. Reserve, Minsmere.

Everything looked set until on the morning of the thirteenth Tim received a telegram from his granny. She was coming to live in Weston Super Mare.
As Bill recalls:
"I had to scrap the whole thing and start all over again. As it turned out, one glance at the map of Weston Super Marc showed me that luck was on our side. Amazingly we had hit upon the very area that for almost half a century had clearly been the movie making mecca of the British film industry."
The whole map was besmattered with the legendary titles of the major epics that had been shot in this seemingly unglamourous corner of Somerset.

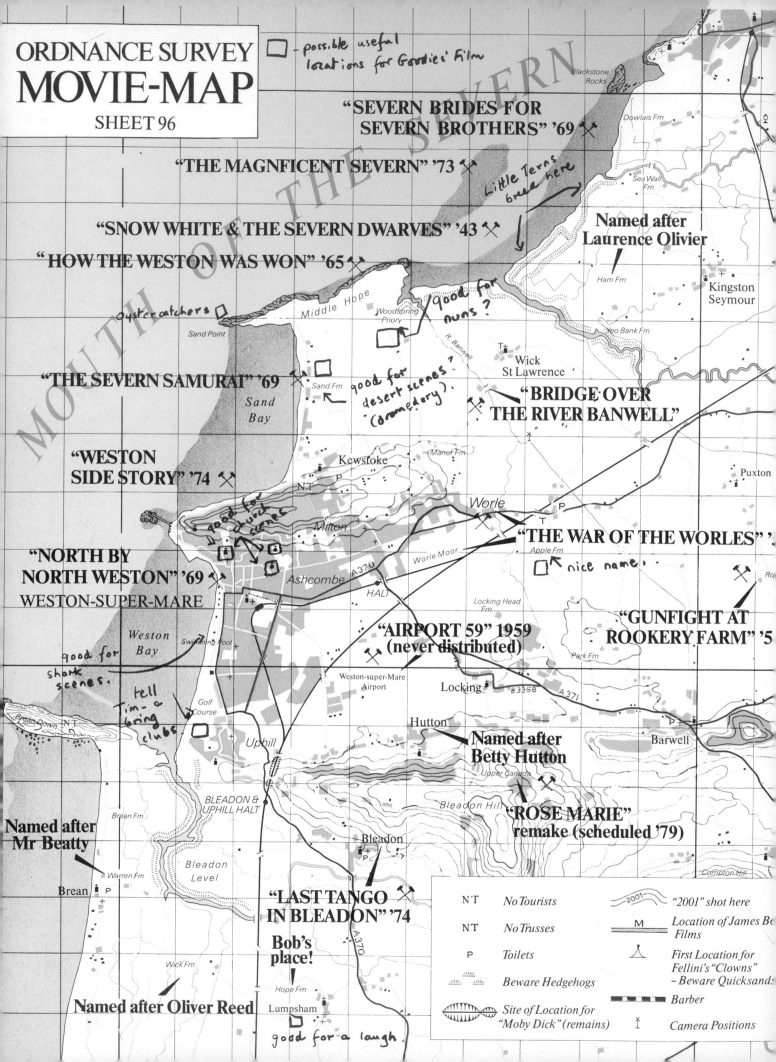

CHAPTER NINE
THE CALL GOES OUT

cindy snow

Dear Mr Oddie,
    We are all very excited that you have agreed to appear in the
Goodies Film. Thanks also for the super designs.
    Mr Brooke-Taylor has asked me to send you a Call Sheet and he
very much hopes that you and he will be able to get together for
a chat, sometime over the next 13 weeks.

    Yours sincerely,

    Cindy Snow

    Cindy Snow.
    Assistant to Director's Assistant.

CALL SHEET

For FIRST DAY of filming of

THE TIM BROOKE- TAYLOR STORY.
(working title)

PRODUCER: Louie Bumce
DIRECTOR: Ken Russell

PART	ARTISTE	CALL	CAR TO PICK UP	MAKE-UP & COSTUME	SPECIAL REQUIREMENTS
TIM	Tim Brooke-Taylor	8.30	Palace Hotel, Weston, straight to location	Hair washed and set ready for arrival of Star	"Travelhome" caravan with large star on door. Colour T.V. and all to be covered with pink fur.
	Oliver Reed	8.30	Palace Hotel, Weston and straight to John O'Groats	Not required	Faulty compass
GRAEME	Nana Mouskouri (and the Athenians)	6.30	No car. The walk will do her good.	Usual tat and silly glasses	Hot and cold running Moussaka.
	Keith Moon	3.30	Mobile padded room. Mr Moon to be taken to hospital and then on to location after release.	Rouge. Straitjacket.	Net and large supply of tranquilisers
BILL	The Bolshoi Ballet	1 am.	or when their performance ends at Raymonds Revue Bar.	Large long wig and enormous beard. Tasteful padding.	Somewhere to defect.
	Or if wet Henry Kissinger	?	Own plane.	Nose job.	Dialogue coach

PART	ARTISTE	TIME	CAR TO PICK UP.	MAKE-UP & COSTUME	SPECIAL REQUIREMENTS
BONZO THE WONDER DOG.	Bert Lancaster and Jon Wayne	8.30	Car to "Bertanjon" Acacia Villas Weston. Driver to pick up Mr Lancaster and Mr Wayne, and put them in the car.	Own skin.	A tree
Stand by "BONZO THE WONDER DOG".	Jack Nicolson James Caan Charles Bronson Donald Sutherland Elliott Gould Michael York Lord Lucan Roger Moore Paul Newman Sean Connery Robert Redford	6.30	To be picked up from The Holiday Inn, Bristol. 3 cars each. 4 cars for Mr Gould. Self-drive car for Mr McQueen (no insurance yet agreed) Roger Moore pick-up from "O.O.Severn" Suite. Mr Connery from "O.O.Wotarefer- ee" suite. Lord Lucan's pick up spot not yet agreed.	Six legged Dromedary skin, All to bring own Wotwigs please.	See accompanying booklet: How to Crawl to Film- stars by Michael Parkinson
CUTE BABY	Mrs B. White (HEINZ)	8.30	Ambulance. Police and Fire to standby	2 doz nappies in shape of Winder- mere and Connis- ton Trusses	Lots of hot water. Coca and Pepsi Cola bottles with teats.
BOX OFFICE CRUMPET	Rita Acapulco	2.30	Car to Marwood Hall If not there on to Dorchester c/o Sheikh Yofist Oasis Suite.	Nun. Make-Up where required.	Bunch of flowers and poodle.
LADY IN LAUNDERETTE (MORE CRUMPET)	Beverley Hills	5.30	The Foreign Office back entrance. Driver to ask for "The Diplomatic Bag"	"De Luxe Windermere and Conniston Black Lace See Thru Honeymoon Truss" and Nun's Habit.	State Secret
CAST OF THOUSANDS	The Yugoslavian Army		Early call.(7 days early April 14th) 5000 tanks to pick up army from barracks in Belgrade and take straight to location. Don't forget to 'go' before you set off, it's a long trip.	No make up except as hordes of savages. Use own boot polish. 36 pairs see- through pantal- oons. 36 Tin- foil bras. 35 Yashmacks. 254 veils.	25,000 bunches of flowers and poodles. 7,000 toothbrushes and paste. 18,000 glasses of water.
	Corporal Skratćanić		From his Granny's house in Zagreb. Tank driver please don't let him leave his teddy behind again.	Mask, Rubber Gloves and Foot- ball boots. The Corporal is a skilled Obstetrician and centrefor- ward for Yugoslavia	Lots and lots of hot water. Dubbin.
TIM'S HAT	Tim's Hat		Securicor to make arrangements.	Fresh fruit and poppies.	Bulletproof Box.
STANDINS FOR Mr Brooke- Taylor	Graeme Garden & Bill Oddie				

Mr Garden and Mr Oddie will also act as standins and stuntmen for Nana Mouskouri (but not the Athenians), Keith Moon, The Bolshoi Ballet, Henry Kissinger, Bert Lancaster, Jon Wayne. They will also act as standin for Standby "Bonzo the Wonder Dog".

TECHNICAL CREW.   The Queen's Own Armoured Photographers to be on
                         location by 6.30 am.

TECHNICAL
REQUIREMENTS.   Nickeromat 15' Zoom Lens
                         "Garbolegs" Tripod
                         10,763,495 matchboxes
                         One button
                         LIGHTS..... all drivers please note that from time
                                     to time they will be required to drive
                                     to certain sites and to switch their
                                     headlights full on.
                         SOUND   Not required on first day but, Graeme
                                     please have your Dictaphone standing
                                     by just in case.

LOCATION
CATERING................by FANNY CRADDOCK (SPUN SUGAR) LTD.

                         TEA BREAKS: 7 am. 9 am. 9.30 am. 11.15 am. 11.45 am.
                         COFFEE BREAKS: 7.15 am. 8 am. 8.30 am. 10 am. 11.30 am.
                         FOOD BREAKS: Bacon rolls, susage, egg, black pudding
                                        Yugoslav rissoles at 7.45 am. 8.15 am.
                                        9 am. (Alternative to tea break) 10.15 am.
                                        10.45 am. 11 am.

                         LUNCH: 12.00 to 15.00 Artists and crew are asked
                                        to be back on the set no later than
                                        17.00 hrs please.

                         SPECIAL DIETS: Please contact Johnny.
                                        (N.B.These breaks are at the discretion of the
                                         Director - but he may be able to include
                                         a few more)

DIRECTIONS TO LOCATION:
        Travel South out of Weston on the A /70. After the third garage
on the left you will come to a pub called "The White Whores".
Ignore this and continue on for half a mile where you will see an
A.A. sign to "Bleadon Flower Show". Follow the Bleadon signs to the
Bleadon Flower Show where the Bleadon Vicar's wife will have further
Bleadon directions for you.
For those driving from Belgrade the above directions still apply
but add at the beginning:- "Drive to Weston Super Mare". N.B.
Along the route discreet bushes have been planted for the sole
use of Mrs B. White.

        GOOD SHOOTING GENTLEMEN!   Tim Brooke-Taylor
                                              (Assistant to Director and Star)

TRANSCRIPT OF CONVERSATION BETWEEN BILL ODDIE AND TIM BROOKE-TAYLOR. TIME:
8 PM. ON EVENING BEFORE FIRST DAY'S SHOOT.

BILL: For one thing I'm not going to be anybody's ****** stand-in.
        And for another thing haven't you forgotten the teeniest
        little detail that might make shooting impossible?

TIM: No.

BILL: Yes you have.

TIM: No I haven't. Just name one thing I've forgotten, just one.

BILL: A Script!

TIM: (Apparently screaming) MUMMY WHERE HAVE YOU PUT MY BLANKET!.

ELEVEN HOURS TO GO BEFORE SHOOTING WAS DUE TO COMMENCE. BUT THE GOODIES
HAD NO SCRIPT. SURELY THIS MUST BE THE END.

THE

Designed and Art Directed by Anthony Cohen

Graphics
Margot Parker, John Leach, Simon Bell, James Campus, Mike Spiller.

Illustration
Anabel Milne, Peter Stebbing, Allard Design Group, Arnaldo Putzu, Denis C. Hawkins, Ken Cox,
Arthur Ranson, Graeme Garden.

Photography
Ken Randall

END

Pictorial Material
Camera Press, John Kobal, Press Association, Spectrum Colour, Radio Times Hulton, Reg Wilson, Ray Daffurn.

Special thanks to
Jemma, Edward Bear, Annie, Casandra, Tom, Lewis, Judy, Derek Mcnally, Lisa, Corin Challenger, Pat Shears

Typesetting
Studio Typesetting, Owl Creative.

CHAPTER TEN
WRITING THE SCRIPT

THE SONG OF KAA-WE-LA, THE SCRIPTWRITER
by Lord Baden-Powell

Cold showers of rain maintain my spirit,
(Um-gaa, um-gaa!)
Here I toil with pen and paper,
(Um-gaa, um-gaa!)
Like a beast of the jungle, there are laws to obey!
Um-gaa Kaa-we-laa!

It must be done!
So speaks Kaa-we-laa!
Though the naughty one within me cries:
(Um-gaa, um-gaa!)
Stuff this for a game of soldiers.

An extract from Making Films for Pleasure and Profit by Lord Baden-Powell

But it was not the end.
In the film world hold ups like this are common enough, due to nothing more than a trivial oversight, the lack of a script. But with only eleven hours to go before shooting started, it was going to be a close run thing. How were they going to churn out ninety minutes worth of Oscar-winning dialogue in the time left?
Tim wasted the first forty minutes gibbering. When Bill finally managed to coax him down from the top of the wardrobe it was clear he wasn't going to be much use for a while – at least until he'd found the blanket, not to mention the hat. The seconds ticked mercilessly by, the sound of the clock echoed by the pacing of Bills' feet as he strode round and round the room like a caged animal, tearing out his hair. Before long he realised that this was pointless, so he started tearing out Tim's hair instead. In next to no time Tim was back on top of the wardrobe, and Bill was forced to content himself with tearing the hair out of a Wotwig. Then suddenly Bill came up trumps! With only eight hours to go till the deadline, he remembered he had once applied to a Correspondence Course in Writing! If he could only find it, that would solve the problem of how to get started on the script. After a desperate search, he found what he was after:

SSFBT Scrimm-Scramm, Farnes, Barnes and T
Correspondence College for Scriptwrite

c/o Flat 843
"Sorento" Vertical Village,
Crewe

A MESSAGE TO OUR CLIENTS.

Dear Client

So you require to be a scriptwriter? Well you are not alone as many people similarly in your position also want to achieve this aim. But of course they are at a disadvantage from the word go. Because they will not have had the advanta over them which you will have had, namely the benefits of a full Scrimm-Scramm Farnes Barnes and Tagg Correspondence course and consequently be able to write marketable scripts which you can sell to Hollywood for Pots and Pots of Money! Stick to it, and send us your subscription on the dot as regular as clockwork, and you will be enjoying the fruits of your talent in next to no time at all. And its oh so easy, once you know how. Which is why we have secured some of the finest writers imaginable to write our lessons. Here is the first lesson, given to you by that famous man of letters Mr Frank Muir.

Happy learning!

Yours Dennis Scrimm-Scramm
KENNETH FARNES
Clive Barnes   P.W. TAGG (esq)

LESSON ONE

by **FRANK MUIR**

HELLO.

You know, many people who want to start a career in scriptwriting come to me for advice. To them I always say the same thing. If you are really serious about your ambition, and you're prepared to put everything into it, then by far the most important single thing to get right is the colour. The pattern may seem to be equally crucial, but I have always found that, if the colour is right, then everything else follows on quite naturally. Once colour and pattern have been chosen, then it is the work of but a moment to knot it neatly round the neck into a stylish, but not floppy, bow. I have always considered it essential to wear a proper hand-tied bow, by the way, so please, none of your appalling ready-made efforts on bits of elastic.

In scriptwriting, as in anything else, one can learn a great deal from the Masters in this particular field. Indeed, writers of all kinds throughout the centuries have worn bow ties. Mark Twain, when writing "Huckleberry Finn" is said to have worn a green bow-tie; Terence Rattigan has quite a selection; Raymond Chandler favoured a dark blue one with white clocks on it; and I've got a pink one.

Of course the novice writer can hardly expect to come up with a masterpiece straight away. Years of experience are needed to acquire the polish of the true craftsman. For example, the writers of that splendidly sophisticated film "The Apartment", Billy Wilder and I. A. L. Diamond, only had one bow-tie between them which they wore on alternate days; Wilder on Monday, Diamond on Tuesday, and so on. As a result, it was many years before either of them could tie a bow that was fit to be seen in urbane and witty society.

But now for more practical advice to the young writer. I have sketched out below a simple diagram which I hope will serve as a guide to the basic steps involved.

Now many of you, like me, no doubt feel that it is high time that an Academy Award was given to the script-writer with the neatest →

PTO

Meanwhile, Tim also went to work. Borrowing a library ticket, he hurried off to the local Library, to look up some books on how to write screenplays.

His researches were surprisingly successful. At the end of a hectic hour browsing among the shelves, he hurried home bearing armfuls of useful volumes. Books like *The Secret of Writing Stupendous Biblical Epics* by Matthew Mark Luke and John, *Spelling made easy* by F. Scott Fitzgerald, and by way of light relief *Just Looning Around!*, the autobiography of Ingmar Bergman.

But most useful of all, Tim had managed to obtain original copies of actual screenplays. By a careful study of these manuscripts, he hoped to be able to work out how to put down on paper the block-buster they needed.

LONDON BOROUGH OF CRICKLEWOOD
Library of books on how to write screenplay

BORROWER'S TICKET 0997734/
Name   *Neil Simon*
Address *77 Sunset Boulevard*
          CRICKLEWOOD
Date   *17.3.73*

This ticket must be produced every time a book on how to write screenplays is borrowed. It also entitles the bearer to drive heavy goods vehicles. (But only if travelling to write a screenplay at the time.)

This ticket has been written by G.P.W.Troate, who is also available for writing speeches, TV series, screenplays, and signs. Previous triumphs include "Wet Paint."

This Library ticket has been a

G.P.W. TROATE PRODUCTION

KING KONG   Shooting Script.   page 137

416: Close up of the girl.   CUT TO:
            GIRL:
      Eeeeeeeeaaaaaaarrrhhh!!

418: Long shot of Kong.   CUT TO:
            KONG:
      Gwwrrrooooooooouuuugh!!

419: Two shot of girl and Kong.   CUT TO:
            GIRL:
      Eeeeeeeeeeeeeeeeeeek!
            KONG:
      Wrrrrraaaaaaaaaauuuuuurrrrghhhh!

420: Tight close-up of girl.   CUT TO:
            GIRL:
      Aaaaaaaaaaaaaaaaaaaaaiiiiiieeeeeeeghcht!
            KONG (OUT OF VISION):
      OooouuuuuuuhhhhhrrrnnngghhhhAAAAAAARGH!!!!

421: Close up of Kong.   CUT TO:
            KONG:
      GrrreeeeaaaaoooooUUUUUUGHEEEAAAAAAANNNHHHH!!!

422: Close up of girl.   CUT TO:
            GIRL:
      Oo-er!

An actual page of the actual shooting script of the actual original version of the actual 'KING KONG'

CUT TO:

137:    Interior.   Krafchik's Villa.   Day.

A man enters from the patio through the half-open french windows. It is
BATTERSBY. He moves carefully across the cluttered living room, nervous,
alert. BATTERSBY is a man of medium height (5'9" or 10") and of
indeterminate age. He could be anything from 25 to 37. In fact he is 38,
and meticulously careful of his appearance. His neatly cut hair is brushed
in the city style, and it is even possible that the bronze highlights in
the distinguished grey are the result of skilful tinting. Despite the sub-
tropical humidity his skin is smooth and dry. His eyes are a deep limpid
brown, the lashes obviously professionally trimmed. He moves with a slight
limp, made more obvious by the involuntary flinching of his knees as he
catches sight of a print of Valpolicella's Madonna and Infant over the fireplace, an automatic reflex which betray's BATTERSBY's early Catholic upbring-
ing, while at the same time the defensive tightening of the three wrinkles at
the corner of each eye pronounces his later rejection of the Faith. His
clothes are smart, crisp, well chosen, beautifully cut, and mauve. When he
speaks, BATTERSBY's voice retains a hint of an Irish lilt, an accent
assimilated long since in the days of his close association with the Jesuit
Fathers who educated him. He looks round the room and clears his throat.

          BATTERSBY:
          Hello?

A shot rings out and BATTERSBY falls dead.

Enter DOBBS, an ordinary sort of bloke.

          DOBBS
       · Coo-er! Well here's a rum go,
          and no mistake.

                    CUT TO:

Valpolicella's Madonna & Child Over The Fireplace

*An actual page of the actual shooting script of the
actual original version of the actual 'At It Again'
by Graham Greene (later re-titled 'Bridge to Yesterday'
by Somerset Maughan.)*

Ten minutes later, things were really moving.

The scene in the office was one of pandemonium as Tim and Bill unpacked crates of books, cartons of manuscripts, bags of correspondence material, and ream upon ream of instructions. They were beginning to survey the accumulated piles of research material with something akin to panic now, because they hardly knew where to start in the task of getting down to write the screenplay itself.

They need not have worried. Behind them in the corner, quietly, almost unnoticed, the Computer chattered intently to itself.

At last, the crunch came. Bewildered by the array of paper that surrounded them, the two Goodies were about to collapse in despair, when from the Computer came the sound of the Timer bell, signifying 'finished'. They looked up, hardly daring to hope, as the door opened and Graeme strode purposefully in, crossed to the Computer, and as he nonchalantly flicked a couple of little knobs, Tim and Bill could hardly restrain their cries of delight; for out of the computer poured word after word, line after line, page after page of screenplay.

Later, over a cup of tea, Graeme explained. He had, it transpired, programmed the computer some days before to scan its memory banks for all the successful ingredients of previous screen successes, and to come up with an all purpose script to suit any movie. This script now lay before them, and as Graeme quickly demonstrated, all they had to do was to tick the ingredient of their choice. The possibilities were endless, as the first page or so revealed – but every single possible combination would be a monster success!

```
COMPUTA SCRIPT-OUT ..................................
.
.......................... RANDOM/SELECT PROG

MULTIPLE CHOICE .............. TICK YOUR SELECTION .....

..................................................

GO ..............................................


THE FILM OPENS ON A COLD DAY IN THE YEAR   843 ...........
                          HOT              1560
                          WET ✓            1776
                          WEDNES           1852
                          SNOWY            1977 ✓
                                           2001


WE SEE A BEDROOM            IN NEW YORK .................
        RACETRACK             PARIS
        CRYPT                 BANGKOK
        TOILET      ✓         CRICKLEWOOD ✓
        KITCHEN  ✓            TRANSYLVANIA
        BATTLEFIELD
        HOT TIN ROOF


TIM     ✓    IS DISCOVERED ALONE.  HE ✓ IS WASHING UP.
BILL ✓                             SHE    DUSTING
GRAEME                             IT     EATING
MAN                                       DRINKING
GIRL                                      SINGING    ✓
DOG                                       BURYING A CORPSE
CITIZEN KANE                              DOING THE OBVIOUS
BAT
DWARF
VAN GOGH


ENTER BILL   ✓      DIALOGUE: OH DEAR WHAT A MESS WE ARE IN
      TIM    ✓
      GRAEME
      MAN
      GIRL
      DOG
      BAT
      DWARF
      SHARK
      GOOFY
```

WOULD YOU BELIEVE IT THE CAT   HAS ONLY GONE AND THROWN UP OVER THE ✓
                     BILL   CARPET ✓
                     TIM   BEEN ARRESTED
                     GRAEME   ✓   FALLEN IN LOVE
                     LASSIE   PASSED WIND
                     BEETHOVEN   ATTACKED PEARL HAR-
                     MR CHIPS   BOUR
                     KING KONG   OPENED A TRUSS BOUT
                                                              -IQUE

AND IT/S ALL BECAUSE OF THAT STEW I COOKED. WHAT.'S TO BE DONE?
                     NICHOLAS PARSONS
                     A CRUSADING SPIRIT
                     CERTAIN TENDENCIES
                     LOVE ✓
                     WAR
                     ILL-FITTING DENTURES
                     ATOM BOMB TESTS

DON'T ASK ME WHAT'S TO BE DONE, TIM   MY OLD CHUM.
                                 BILL
                                 GRAEME
                                 POPE PAUL
                                 BUSTER
                                 DENNIS THE DROMEDARY ✓
                                 HARPO
                                 HANDSOME
                                 ADOLF

BUT THAT REMINDS ME I AM FORGETTING YOU HAVE NOT MET MY FIANCE/E ✓-

DO YOU NOT THINK HE HAS THAT CERTAIN SOMETHING?
                 SHE ✓   CHARM
                 IT   A SMASHING WOGGLE
                          MAGNIFICENT AMBERSONS
                          A CHANCE
                          NERVE
                          SHARP TEETH
                          A NATURAL SENSE OF RHYTHM ✓

BUT BEFORE HE ✓ CAN REPLY THEY ARE INTERRUPTED BY A KNOCK.
           SHE   FORCED TO STRIP
           IT   INVADED BY GENGHIS KHAN
                                     BURIED
                                     ATTACKED BY SAVAGES ✓
                                     CUT UP INTO LITTLE BITS
                                     ON THE ROAD TO MOROCCO

                                     EATEN
                                     POSTED OVERSEAS
                                     IN BED
                                     OVER-RATED

CUT TO. ....

A DINGY ATTIC.   ENTER GRAEME AND HIS PARTNER TIM.
       BASEMENT   TIM   GRAEME
       PRAIRIE   BILL   BILL
       OFFICE   RODGERS   TRIGGER
       PALACE   TOM   HAMMERSTEIN
       BEACH-HEAD ✓   LAUREL   MR HYDE
       THEATRE   LONE RANGER   EMU
       NEW ENGLAND RESORT   BATMAN   DR WATSON
       CORRAL   ABBOT ✓   MOTHER SUPERIOR ✓
                           LORD SNOOTY   NICOLSON

SLOWLY AND CAREFULLY THEY BEGIN TO UNFOLD THE PLANS ....
                                   UNDRESS
                                   EAT LUNCH
                                   MAKE L+VE
                                   HUNT A GIANT SHARK
                                   HUNT A GIANT DWARF
                                   SING ✓

Tim and Bill of course were overjoyed, and Graeme of course was very very smug indeed.

But now they knew that the chore of dashing off a script was out of the way, they could apply themselves seriously to the more important aspects of the project . . .

The Hammer Blood Chart

Want to get that oh-so-important shade just right?
Want to avoid the **NIGHTMARE** of blood that *clashes* with the *costume?*
Then don't be a **CLOT!**
Don't just make up your mind on the **SPURT** of the moment!
Let **HAMMER BLOOD** help you to choose the colour that suits the mood. Blood for every occasion that will draw appreciative screams, gasps and retches. Do it right with **HAMMER BLOOD** – after all, nobody wants to be a **SILLY BLEEDER!**

Dracula's Delight

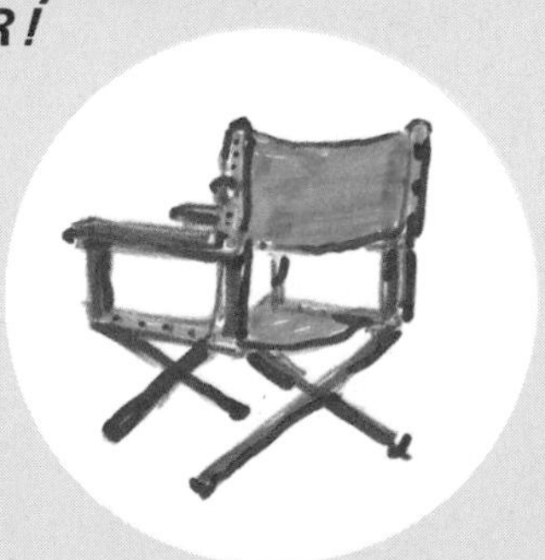

Blood Bath

Corpuscle Punishment

Hello Suckers

Horrific Haemoglobin

Wot Wig

Royal Blue

Midnight Feast

Heart Broken

Rare Stake

Blood Count

Kensington Gore

UFO Juice

Bloody Fool

Red Mist

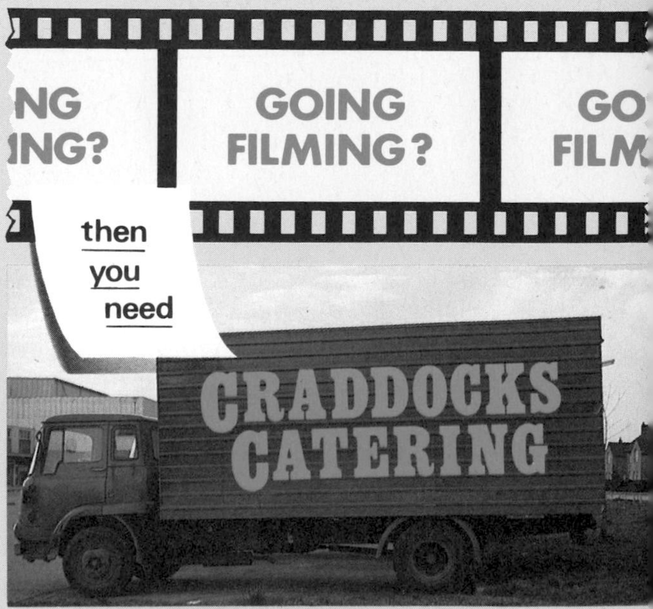

Uncle Rhesus

In Lighter Vein

Peckinpah Pink

Available by the bucket.

CHAPTER ELEVEN
THE FIRST DAY

It was the twenty-first of June. It was dawn.

The Great Gaffer in the sky aimed his celestial follow-spot towards the tiny village of Wick St Lawrence, just outside Weston Super Mare. The shimmering sycamores in the old churchyard filtered the harshness of the beam as it scanned down the cobbled highstreet. Finally it settled. The village square was bathed in limelight – a stage patiently awaiting the arrival of the stars.

Through that spotlight, within the next half hour, were to pass a pageant of players that would've caused Lew Grade to wee himself.

But not the milkman of Wick St Lawrence. The pressure of anticipation left his bladder utterly composed. He didn't even bother to look up, as the quirky syncopation of tripping feet told him that a Six-Legged Dromedary was passing by.

"Oh *that* old thing!" he thought to himself.

Only last year he'd delivered 596 pints to Sand Bay, where they were shooting 'The Planet of the Dromedaries'.

"Its not as if any of them can act," he muttered.

Mind you, he might have mollified his criticism had he been aware that inside this particular dromedary were Jack Nicholson, James Caan, Donald Sutherland, Elliott Gould, Michael York, Roger Moore, Paul Newman, Sean Connery, Robert Redford and Steve McQueen. But the milkman didn't know, so he didn't look up – not even when a frantic figure scampered through the spotlight in pursuit of the dappled beast, crying: "Wait for me, wait for me".

"Charles Bronson", thought the milkman.

He was right. He'd seen it all before; and he knew what was coming next.

"Creak-squeek-clang ... creak-squeek-clang ..."

Accurately he analysed and identified; 'Leather boots .. surgical canvas ... bayonets ... perfectly rhythmic ... highly disciplined ... Yugoslavian Army.'

Through the village square they marched, the early sun glancing off their Wot-wigs. A thousand carrot-topped robots, every member securely trussed, by courtesy of *Windermere and Coniston*.

"Oh well, nice to see they're still working".

He had delivered countless gallons to *The Guns of Puxton and Worle* (1969) and *The Bridge Over the River Banwell* (remake, 1972).

'Always good value, the Yugoslavian Army. Drink six pints a day. Tito's orders.'

The milkman was hoping to become a movie mogul himself, and one more really extravagant epic would get through enough gold-top to earn him the wherewithal. Since he'd been lucky enough to land a round that covered the Movie-making Mecca of the South West, he reckoned he knew a thing or two about what should go into a box office smasheroo. After all, be honest, he'd seen a few right stinkers shot round here. If *he* were producing, he'd give 'em a real film. Actually this one seemed to be shaping up fairly nicely.

"Let's see" he surmised, "a dromedary, Charles Bronson, Yugoslavian Army ... now, if they've got any sense at all they'll get the whole of the bleedin' Bolshoi Ballet."

Even as he mused, his conjecture was ruptured by the strain of *The Nutcracker*. Now he did look up, in time to see the 'lollipop-man' stopping the first hay-wain of the morning, to allow the whole of the bleedin' Bolshoi Ballet to pirouette their way across the zebra-crossing. Even the milkman was impressed. This was clearly going to be 'some movie'!

Flushed with the accuracy of his predictions, the milkman risked casting himself in the role of 'master of ceremonies', and the grannies of Wick St. Lawrence leapt from their waterbeds as he confidently announced the arrival of: "Mr. Jon Wayne, . . and Mr. Bert Lancaster!"

Every lace curtain in the high street drew back, and a dozen pairs of trembling lorgnettes beheld . . . the ponciest little Shihtzu you ever did see. But the milkman wasn't fazed. He'd recognise that mince anywhere.

"Hi Jon, Hi Bert", called the milkman.

The Shihtzu waved. And a dozen grannies swooned.

Jon Wayne   **Bert Lancaster**

And so the parade continued: the most illustrious all-star cast ever assembled in the history of motion pictures.

Heinz, the greatest and newest child-star of them all, still snugly coiled in the protective womb of his mother, Mrs. B. White; Nana Mouskouri and her Athenians; Graeme Garden and his glasses; Bill Oddie and his binoculars; Tim Brooke Taylor and his hat!

Yep, this was going to be 'some movie' . . . or was it?

Meanwhile, on the second-team pitch of the Wick St. Lawrence Rugby Football Club, the camera crew of the Queens Own Armoured Photographers were having a little difficulty assembling the eighty foot crane that they had borrowed from Liverpool docks, in order to lift the fifteen foot Zoom Lens up to the level of the four foot camera tripod. They solved the problem by digging a four foot pit, dropping the tripod into it, rolling the lens along the half way line and across the top of the pit, so that it lay just above the tripod and could thus be attached to the camera. The crew would have to work within the confines of the pit but they seemed happy enough, since, as their elderly sergeant pointed out, it reminded them of the good old days in the trenches. As if to prove the point, he whipped out his mouth-organ,

rendered a quick chorus of *Keep the Home Fires Burning* and declared he was 'going over the top'. An unwise decision, as it turned out. The Colonel of the newly-arrived Yugoslavian Army had already mistaken the zoom lens for a mortar-point, and surrounded it. Now, on spotting the sergeant leaping from the 'bunker' waving a white flag (his lens-cloth actually), the Colonel suffered a similar fit of nostalgia, and blew his head off!

It seemed a trivial enough incident at the time; but looking back, it was perhaps a strange portent of the many mishaps that were to plague the whole making of the film.

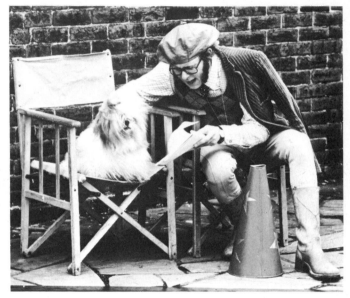

The rest of the first day was not without incident. In fact, it was one bleedin' disaster after another.

Even as the headless Sergeant protested at his rough treatment as best he could – by dropping dead – more trouble arrived in the downright disruptive but undeniably voluptuous shape of . . . Miss Rita Acapulco! Miss Rita was used to men losing their heads over her, and so she was not unduly surprised when the sergeant's flew past her left shoulder. With the reflexes of a Barry John, she caught it and drop-kicked it through the posts – the swing of her hips sending the Wick St Lawrence three quarters the wrong way - and turned to face the Yugoslavian Army. The Yugoslavian Army was not familiar with Rita Acapulco which was surprising, since every one else had been. Rumour had it (and so did Rita, often) that she had only got where she was by offering her body to Film Producers. This was *not* true. She was *anybody's*. Now, on the morning of the twenty first, there she stood, thighs akimbo, tempting and testing the safely-strapped manhood of a whole regiment. Even she could not have anticipated their response – NOTHING! Nary a twinge. Rank upon rank, seemingly unmoved. Paragons of self-discipline, not a flicker of emotion disturbed the stony features of

"Going . . ."   "Going . . ."   "Going . . ."   "TWANNG!!!"

the Yugoslavian Army. Only the twanging of a thousand trusses betrayed their arousal. Boing . . . boing . . . boing . . . boing . . . boing boing boing . . .

Rita's eyelashes palpitated with anticipation, like a pair of Tarantulas poised to pounce on a thousand flies. Every snapping buckle, every pinging elastic strap was an overture of lust to her ears. But this was a military advance never to be consummated. Amidst a cacophany like the Third Movement of the Toy Symphony, the reputation of the Windermere and Coniston Truss and Surgical Appliance Company collapsed – and so did the Yugoslavian Army. Within seconds, a thousand bronzed heroes shrank, shrivelled and crumpled into a thousand impersonations of Rumplestiltskin. Bill ordered new trusses, and Graeme began a rewrite. But Rita was rampant. She had her reputation to think of, and it was in grave danger of becoming decent. With a monumental misjudgement of character, she lunged towards the Male Corps of the Bolshoi Ballet. To a man, they turned and fled. And the man they turned and fled to, turned and fled too.

Rita was mortified. To be fair, the Dromedary seemed willing enough, but even Rita drew the line at animals; a fact clearly unappreciated by Bonzo the Wonder Dog, who launched himself at Rita with an enthusiasm that, in one bound, utterly annihilated Bill's theory of 'sexual deviation in theatrical midgets'. Bonzo was clearly no 'gay-dog'. And to prove it, like a ferret after a rabbit, the little Shihtzu shot up Rita's hot-pants; from which grotto of delight he could only be extracted by 'smoking him out' – an incident which gave the name 'hot-pants' a whole new validity. Jon Wayne and Bert Lancaster emerged, tired, charred, but happy, to be greeted by a cheer and a threat that if there was any more of 'that sort of thing', they would be sent to the vet to be 'seen to'.

It hadn't been a good morning, but during the rest of the day things got marginally worse. No sooner had the Army been refitted, than Miss Beverly Hills turned up, and so did the Army . . . and twang went another thousand trusses.

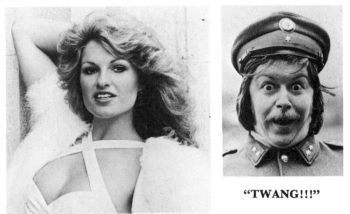

"TWANG!!!"

By the afternoon, the weather had turned rather less warm, but despite the snow, everyone seemed reasonably content changing behind the bushes; until the arrival of Mr. Brooke Taylor, who required no more than a couple of sentences to earn himself his subsequent 'nom de filme' of 'Mr. Tact'. He garnered little sympathy during ten minutes stomping around in a mink-lined anorak complaining that there was 'too much green' in his colour T.V. set; and provoked a total mutiny when he told a shivering blue-humped dromedary:

"Heaven knows, I'd love to invite you into my heated caravan, but I can hardly get at my quilted couch for crates of champagne and brandy".

* * * * * * * * * * *

All work was suspended until every single member of the cast was provided with his or her own caravan, couch, colour T.V., and six crates of booze. Unfortunately, the Rugby Club car-park was being used, as there was a first-team game that evening, so all the caravans had to be parked on the second-team pitch.

Thus the camera, being immovably stuck in its pit, had its viewpoint somewhat restricted – to vertically upwards. At least this enabled Bill to get a nice shot of an Arctic Tern flying overhead.

The second team pitch

The afternoon limped towards evening. Wick St. Lawrence lost 15-6 to Lympsham, and the sun was just sinking behind the northern goalposts when a 6 litre Vauxhall Interceptor, in the shape of a giant Coca Cola Bottle, drove up, pulling behind it what appeared to be a padded cell on wheels. In the cell was Keith Moon. In the Bottle, Ken Russell. It was mooted to Mr. Russell that there were about two minutes 'shooting light' left, and wasn't it a bit bleedin' late for the Director to roll up?

Russell, with a philosophical logic that would have befitted his more philosophical and logical namesake (Jane), explained that experience had taught him that nothing *ever* gets done on the first day, so he didn't usually bother to turn up at all; and if we'd all had any sense we wouldn't have turned up either; and we could have all arrived on the second day, and saved a whole lot of aggro!

So accepting the word of experience, and agreeing that we shouldn't have had a first day at all, we decided to make the best of it, by ending it. At half past six we all went to bed.

An hour later the caravan site was still. Nothing had been achieved – but we were not too despondent, as nothing had been attempted. Now all seemed peaceful enough. Graeme went round conducting a final security check. His precious zoom-lens towered majestically upwards from the camera-pit, its red light flashing a warning to low flying aircraft. Graeme buried the sergeant between the legs of the tripod (he was sure that was what he would have wanted) and as he patted down the soil, where the head should have been, he noticed that one of the tripods silver limbs was now encrusted with a few crimson droplets of dried blood. Graeme wept a silent tear – it'd *never* come off.

As he wandered through the labyrinth of curtained caravans, Graeme paused awhile. Wistfully, he imagined Nana Mouskouri unpinning her hair, taking off her glasses, and crashing around trying to find the bed. Softly, he bellowed at The Athenians to 'put a sock in it'. He noted the synchronised muffled clunk of a thousand falling trusses, followed by a thousand sighs.

He looked up and around and smiled at the motley silhouettes that festooned the clothes lines and goalposts, dozens of pairs of tights; diaphanous tutus, spread like spiders webs; the dromedary skin, dangling from a cross-bar, like a gigantic sloth; a whole cluster of wot-wigs, still exuding an eery gingery glow like a pack of luminous bush-babies; and there was one of Rita Acapulco's bras, swinging like a pair of twin hammocks (they'd accommodated a few sailors in their time) and, heavens! – he must tell Bill this – wasn't that a Tawny Owl nesting in the right cup? Graeme cupped his hands and attempted a seductive 'woo hoo'. There was no response. He crept closer. Yes, he could just make out a pair of round eyes staring unblinkingly at him, But no, it wasn't a Tawny Owl. It was the sergeant's head. Graeme chuckled at his error, and picking up a bucketful of Brown Ale, he set off to perform his final chore – feeding Keith Moon.

As he approached the padded cell, he realised something was wrong. He listened for the crazed muffled thumping that would signify that the arch-raver was safely confined. But the night was still. No thumping, no sounds of muted looning. No burps, no farts, no throwing up. Only the creak of an open door as it swung ominously in the breeze.

KEITH MOON HAD ESCAPED!

CHAPTER TWELVE

Was the film cursed? Only Graeme knew the real extent of the danger. Keith Moon hadn't looned for *three weeks*! It was Russell's master plan. For three weeks he'd kept him away from Oliver Reed. For *three weeks* he hadn't allowed him so much as a hotel room to smash, or a photographer to pee on. It was all being saved for the movie. He'd had it all planned: last day of shooting – Westminster Abbey – two hundred nuns, a hundred and fifty midgets, thirty five gallons of paraffin, a box of matches and . . . Keith Moon! The loon of a lifetime! Whoosh! Thirty six choirboys burnt to death, Westminster Abbey razed to the ground. The WHO would do the soundtrack, Keith would get 'life', and Ken would get the Oscars! But now . . . KEITH MOON HAD ESCAPED! The whole film was in danger. In five minutes concentrated looning he could destroy the entire location, the props, the equipment, the stars, the lot. Graeme was certain of one thing: the unit *must not know*. Total panic would be inevitable. But where was Moon? What was he doing? At that instant, a hideous cacophany told Graeme exactly where Moon was, and precisely what he was doing – and *he wasn't raving . . . he wasn't even looning . . . much worse!* He was *playing the drums!*

It wasn't hard to find him, but it seemed impossible to get at him. Barricaded behind the biggest and most redundant drum kit in the world, he seemed impregnable. By this time the whole unit was up and out. Strong men were going mad; weak men were dancing. Something had to be done. Graeme thought quickly, took a deep breath, and called for a 'humane killer'. There were cries of "No No!" and "Shame".

Graeme thought again –

"All right – an inhumane killer!"

Two thousand cheers rent the air.

A thousand rifles were raised to Yugoslavian shoulders. They fired. The fusillade was inaudible over the drum solo, and so were the screams of anguish as the bullets thudded against the skins of eighteen bass-drums, rebounded, and wiped out the first two ranks.

Mercilessly, Moon drummed on, showing a callous disregard for life, sanity and music.

But his downfall was nigh. As his solo reached fever pitch, more and more cymbals crashed around him, more and more drum skins were shattered under the assault of his savage sticks, tom toms were hurled aside, and finally he let out a triumphant cry that Bill recognised as the Looner's distinctive call of "Oioioioioioi-ooooaaaaaargh!"

He knocked the whole kit flying and left himself perched meekly on his drum stool.

A sitting duck.

"Splat!"

Tim's custard-pie hit home. A weeping Ken Russell led Moon back to his padded cell. Sadly the Director muttered to himself: "Another soddin' masterpiece down the drain. If this kind of thing keeps happening I shall have to start working with proper actors."

It was clear that Ken Russell would show very little further interest in the making of *The Goodies Film*. Perhaps their luck had changed at last?

The Milk Break

After the Milk Break

CHAPTER THIRTEEN
A CHAPTER OF DISASTERS

Never work with children and animals ... or midgets, armies, starlets, ballet dancers, Greeks, nuns, Ken Russell, or actors.

On second thoughts, never work.

Lord Baden-Powell

An extract from Making Films for Pleasure and Profit by Lord Baden-Powell

Day 2

Overnight it rained heavily, but by dawn it was clear and sunny. The unit was harshly awakened by the sound of shrill cavorting, which they correctly suspected emanated from Jon Wayne and Bert Lancaster. Bill was all for sending them to the vet that instant, but even he was truly charmed when they were eventually located splashing happily in the coupled baths of Rita Acapulco's pendant brassiere, whose cups were r ow truly overflowing. The child-like innocence of their play was only mildly tainted by the fact that they were using the sergeant's head as a beach ball.

The unit surveyed the almost poetic damage the rain had caused. The dangling dromedary dripped constantly, as if afflicted with perpetual cystitis.

Beneath it, Rita was taking a shower, oblivious of the unsavoury nature of the image.

Crystalled tuttus glistened, spangled with moisture. Clearly the Dance of the Arthritic Swan was surely soon to be added to the Bolshoi's repertoire. Beneath the colony of wot-wigs, the grass appeared to have rusted, yet in the warming sun their fiery lustre, far from having bled away, glowed with a fresh intensity equal to flame itself. The illusion was all too convincing to Tim who.

mistaking the rising steam for smoke, called the Fire Brigade, who promptly drowned the wigs and the rest of the newly-dried unit with a barrage of hose-pipes. The wigs proved as retentive as sponges, and the Yugoslavian Army moved even more stiffly than usual as the constant trickle seeped down their backs and rusted the very buckles on which their deportment depended. But there was work to be done – a film to be shot, and already they were behind schedule.

Graeme produced the first page of his Computa-Script.
" SCENE ONE
THE FILM opens on a WET day in the year 1977.
We see a KITCHEN in CRICKLEWOOD
BILL is discovered alone. He is SINGING.
enter TIM."
It seemed simple enough.

Ken Russell *still* refused to appear. He argued that since yesterday's first day had been discounted, *today* was now the first day, and, since he never bothered with first days, he wouldn't appear till tomorrow.

Graeme promptly voted himself Director and began to logically consider the problems of the script. It was not as simple as it seemed.

lights!   **camera!**   **action!**   **cut.**

For a kick off, it was a nice sunny day, and everyone and everything was now dry as snuff. The Fire Brigade was instantly recalled and the team worked for the rest of the day under an artificial deluge that would have had Noah reaching for his life-jacket. Next, how to convey that the kitchen was in Cricklewood? It was finally resolved that the information should be incorporated into Bill's song, which was amended from *I'll build a Stairway to Paradise* to *I'm in a Kitchen in Cricklewwod.*

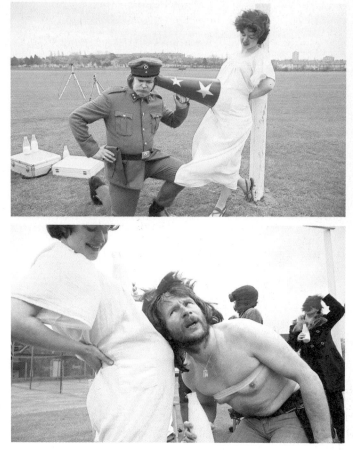

Owing to the paucity of camera-angles available to a zoom-lens stuck vertically in a four-foot pit, and surrounded by caravans, it was clear that for anything to be visible at all, the kitchen would have to be suspended beneath a hot-air balloon, tethered to the rugby post, which would unavoidably be just visible in the lower left corner of the frame, but could perhaps be disguised as a standard-lamp. It then remained for 'Bill' – alias the Bolshoi Ballet – to shin up the Rugby post and swing onto the set. Graeme declared that the philosophical dispute as to whether forty seven could be 'discovered alone' was 'intellectual claptrap'. If just *one*

of them could get up the pole, he, or she, or it would play Bill, and that was that. Unfortunately, in a marxist ballet troupe, if one dancer is going to fall flat on his bum, then so are the other forty six. And they did. That evening the whole lot defected back to Russia.

They were now twenty two days behind schedule. Heinz, the newest and greatest child star, still incarcerated inside the inflexible tum of Mrs. B. White was ten days overdue. Half the cast had gone home. Ken Russell hadn't yet appeared. But it was now that the troubles *really* began.

The Defection

Another Milk Break

After another Milk Break

Day 23

For twenty three days Bill, the rest of the wardrobe department, and the Wick St. Lawrence front-row had been trying to squeeze Charles Bronson into the fifth leg of the dromedary. After that first night's rain, it had shrunk – not a lot – but enough to cause problems. Most of the stars had got in O.K., though Michael York had only been admitted by way of an unseemly aperture that was never meant for entrance. Many went in – nobody had come out. It couldn't have been pleasant in there, and frankly, why Charles Bronson didn't count himself lucky, they couldn't understand. But professional jealousy dims men's judgements. In Charles's case, perhaps, there was never much judgement to dim. He had set his heart on the fifth leg. Indeed, a muffled rumour had escaped from the left nostril that the occupant of the fifth leg had snuffed it several days ago. But there was no way of extracting further information, or the corpse, until the dromedary had shot its scenes. We certainly weren't going to make any incisions, and risk further delays.

But what do to with Charles? There is a saying chalked upon lavatory wall of the Wick St. Lawrence Rugby Club: *A good big 'un will always lick a good little 'un.* So why not *two* little 'uns? No one *wanted* to hurt the feelings of Jon Wayne and Bert Lancaster – except Bill, who had never forgiven them for having such a good time in Rita Acapulco's hot pants – but there was no choice. To Tim fell the unpleasant task of recasting.

MEMO: Re: The part of BONZO THE WONDER DOG.
JON WAYNE AND BERT LANCASTER WILL BE REPLACED BY CHARLES BRONSON

Jon and Bert took the news like true professionals. They bit Tim on the ankle, did a large 'naughty fido' in his hat and scampered off, taking their Shihtzu skin with them. The loss of the skin was a bit of a blow, but it was decided to offer the part to Charles Bronson anyway. Graeme amended the script accordingly.

CUT.   SPRING   DAY

INTERIOR LOG CABIN

288   LONG SHOT. Bill's p.o.v. Tim finishes his packing. He is clearly frightened. Graeme is trying to calm him with a croquet mallet.

289   CLOSE SHOT. BRONSON the Wonder MAN is sleeping curled up by the fire. Suddenly he cocks his ear. Camera pans to the window to see hordes of savages.

290   CLOSE SHOT. Bill looks scared.

          BILL
          We're all going to die.

291   2-SHOT. Graeme is trying to look calm. Tim is busily looking in his suitcase for a suitable pair of brown trousers.

          GRAEME

          Of course we're not going to die. BRONSON will save us.
          Won't you boy?

292   CLOSE SHOT BRONSON The Wonder MAN shakes his coat and bounces around scenting action.

          BRONSON
          Woof.

293   2-SHOT. Graeme proud and satisfied, pats BRONSON who rolls over on his back to have his tummy tickled.

          GRAEME

          My god I swear he understands every word I say. Go to
          it old fellow.

294   LONG SHOT. BRONSON The Wonder MAN his eyes alight and his nose wet drops his bone and leaps through the unopened window.

          BRONSON
          Woof. Woof.
                                         AUTUMN   NIGHT

EXTERIOR OF LOG CABIN

295   LONG SHOT. BRONSON pausing for a moment by a large lampost streaks off to confront the hordes of savages. He starts to herd them like a sheep MAN

          BRONSON
          Woof.

          SAVAGES

          Umbalaba! It's BRONSON the Wonder MAN . Cripes!

    The savages turn and flee, but BRONSON is caught by a stray spear in one of his hind legs.

296   MEDIUM CLOSE SHOT. The light has gone from BRONSON'S eyes. His nose is dry.

          BRONSON

          Woofeeaargh!

    He makes a quite almost inaudible whining sound, rolls over on his back and all his legs stick straight up in the air.

The script was sent off immediately in a taxi. Five days later came the reply. Charles Bronson had turned down the part. Arrogant git!

Day 28
Now twenty eight days behind schedule, in a fit of inspired casting Tim solved the immediate dilemma. Enter: Bonzo, the Wonder Dromedary!

Day 29 and Day 30
The defections of the Bolshoi Ballet, Jon Wayne, Bert Lancaster and Charles Bronson meant we could do away with fifty caravans, which enabled the zoom-lens to be tilted back onto the horizontal, and reveal vastly greater shooting horizons. The rest of the caravans were reparked, so that, by shooting past them, we were able to utilize the almost limitless location possibilities of the Gents Bog of the Wick St. Lawrence Rugby Club, which was to feature, in various scenes, as the Taj Mahal, The Kremlin, a kitchen in Cricklewood and the Gents Bog of the Wick St. Lawrence Rugby Club.

The Kremlin

Although the dromedary lacked something in visual canine authenticity, it revealed an astonishing gift of impersonation, and soon learnt to sit up and beg, 'go fetch', 'die for the queen', and lift its legs, in any one of a dozen permutations.

The Yugoslavian Army looked frankly stunning in their yashmaks and belly dancing gear; and diligently

resolved, perhaps to advantage. When it came to the shark fighting scene, Nana Mouskouri rather soppily demanded a 'stand-in'. Graeme obliged. The shark then demanded equal rights. So Bill 'stood-in' for the shark. Both Nana and the shark enjoyed watching so much, that they refused to do any more scenes. It was agreed that Graeme would stand in for Nana (who was,

rehearsed the Dance of the Seven Surgical Appliances. Even The Athenians did all one could have hoped of them, by keeping out of the whole thing – taking it in turns to smoke and pace up and down outside the caravan of Mrs. B. White, who was now eighteen days overdue.

There were minor problems: but even these were

of course, playing Graeme) for the rest of the shooting, though *her* name would naturally still appear on the credits. The shark, however, became so incensed by Bill's overacting that it asked for its name to be taken off the credits, and went off to audition for Jacques Cousteau. At last, everything seemed to be going just fine. Until . . .

Day 38

Ken Russell re-appeared. It had to happen – a man who sniffs out nuns like Don Revie sniffs out left backs; and today they were due to shoot the nun scene. It wasn't a big nun scene – there weren't a *lot* of nuns in it – be honest, two. Rita Acapulco and Beverly Hills. Even before Ken arrived there was trouble. Rita refused to appear on the set if Beverly was wearing the same costume. Bill patiently explained that it wouldn't be the *same* costume, they would have one each. They said that was even worse.

"How could people tell them apart? All starlets walk the same, pout the same, and are dubbed the same.The only way you can tell one from another is if they look different." Bill riposted (which he tends to do when he gets worked up).

"But you all *look* the same as well! And anyway, a nun is a nun is a nun. So there!"

Beverley and Rita waiting for the set to be cleared before dressing up as Nuns.

For once, Rita and Bervely agreed with each other. With one voice. (provided by an unknown actress who dubbed for them both) they spoke:

"We are not wearing these clothes. We are not wearing ANY clothes. We haven't worn any clothes for six films, and we're not going to resort to doing 'that sort of thing' now."

For the first time in thirty eight days, Ken Russell showed interest. If there was one thing better than a nun, it was a naked nun, and if there was one thing better than a naked nun – it was *two* naked nuns. Better still, four thousand naked nuns. But we could work with two, he could use a multi-image lens.

"You are *not* getting undressed" asserted Bill.

"But it's in the contract!" screamed the starlets. "It's here in Black and White".

"Right. Black and White. Nuns. O.K?" retorted Bill. "No, look. It distinctly says 'CLOTHES – NONE'."

"It says: 'CLOTHES – NUN!' Good God, you can't even spell!"

"We are not here because of our spelling, we are here because of our tits. And we are now going to show them!"

"Right on!" yelled Ken. "Or rather, right off! Off! Off!" A thousand Yugoslavian voices took up the chant. The Athenians struck up with *The Stripper*, and Rita and Beverly prepared to drop their habits.

"No no!" cried Bill. "The Army's doing the Casbah scene this afternoon and we're running short of trusses. Tim, Help!"

'Mr Tact' spoke up: "Listen girls, *please* wear clothes. Nuns always wear clothes. Always . . . even in the bath. It's artistically valid. It's what the script calls for. Look, I promise it'll all be very tastefully shot. I swear we won't cut in any footage of real clothed nuns later. Honest! Just give us thirty seconds of you – with clothes on."

Rita and Beverly actually blushed; "But people'll stare at us!"

"All right, we'll clear the set!"

Ken went purple: "If you don't get 'em showing a bit of bum, I'm off this film once and for all again!"

Tim paused, almost a second.

"Clear the set!"

It was a historic scene. Rita Acapulco, and Beverly Hills on the same set at the same time, both entirely invisible. Perhaps after all, this really *was* going to be some movie.

ommunity
ll familial
et accom-
ntres for
urpose-
lel of a
venture

first
nd to
well
lead.'

vho
ion
the
bt
m
ns
z
/1
o
e
t.
v
l

ANYONE TAKING HOLY ORDERS?
–well, make ours a double! Here's a couple of hot gospellers that would surely go down a treat, and no mistake. Comely Rita Acapulco tells us she's a "lay-sister" – well, you said it, darling! Nubile Beverley Hills has only recently taken the veil – any tickets for the unveiling? – and she hopes to become a Mother Superior (better stay off that pill, dear!)

"Get thee to a nunnery" – wow! Just show us the queue. We'd love to get 'cloister' these two any time – and that's a confession we don't mind making.
Bev and Rita have recently appeared in the Goodies' new film, The Benny Hill Show, The Little Sisters of Mercy Exotic Revue, Raymond's Revue Bar, and are set for a forthcoming season at The Crutchbar, Amsterdam . . .

CHAPTER FOURTEEN
"OR WAS IT?"

All the time, as shooting continued, Graeme was editing. He was also acting, *and* he was directing. It would probably have proved too much for most men. It was *certainly* too much for Graeme. As the days passed he suffered an ever-confusing crisis of identity. At various times, he kept himself waiting for two hours; slapped his own face; and finally vowed he would never work with himself again. Two thirds of him walked out! He never did really decide *which* two thirds. But, in any event, at noon on the forty third day, he emerged from his caravan – entangled in sellotape, wearing eyeshade, and a tulle evening gown – and holding aloft . . . **the first reel!** At last! **the first reel.** The twitching nose of Bonzo the Wonder Dromedary soon sniffed it out, and up he bounded, his tail (played by Sean Connery) wagging furiously. As deftly as a retriever carrying a wounded Mallard, Bonzo's velvetine jaws transported the silver film canister, and a couple of Graeme's fingers . . . off to the censor. The unit took a milk break . . . and waited. Two days later Bonzo was back. Between his legs – his tail. Between his teeth – a plain envelope. In the envelope – our next set-back . . .

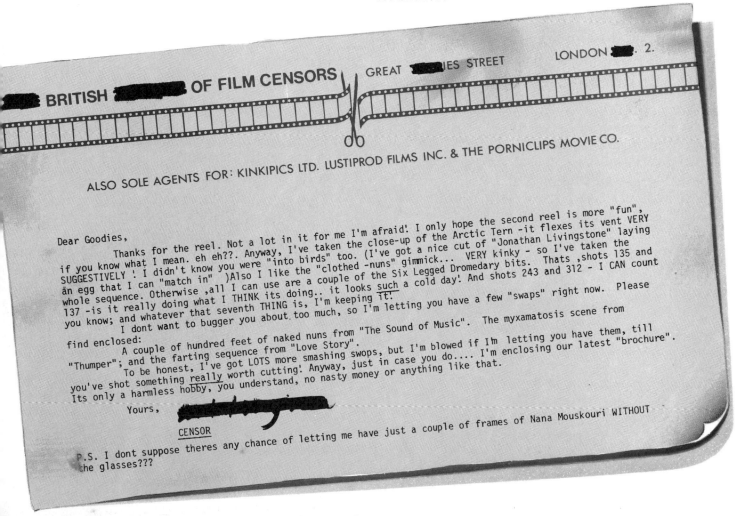

LONDON 2.

BRITISH ████ ████ OF FILM CENSORS GREAT ████ IES STREET

ALSO SOLE AGENTS FOR: KINKIPICS LTD. LUSTIPROD FILMS INC. & THE PORNICLIPS MOVIE CO.

Dear Goodies,
        Thanks for the reel. Not a lot in it for me I'm afraid! I only hope the second reel is more "fun", if you know what I mean. eh eh??. Anyway, I've taken the close-up of the Arctic Tern -it flexes its vent VERY SUGGESTIVELY ! I didn't know you were "into birds" too. (I've got a nice cut of "Jonathan Livingstone" laying an egg that I can "match in")Also I like the "clothed -nuns" gimmick... VERY kinky - so I've taken the whole sequence. Otherwise ,all I can use are a couple of the Six Legged Dromedary bits. Thats ,shots 135 and 137 -is it really doing what I THINK its doing.. it looks such a cold day! And shots 243 and 312 - I CAN count you know; and whatever that seventh THING is, I'm keeping it!
        I dont want to bugger you about too much, so I'm letting you have a few "swaps" right now. Please find enclosed:
        A couple of hundred feet of naked nuns from "The Sound of Music". The myxamatosis scene from "Thumper"; and the farting sequence from "Love Story".
        To be honest, I've got LOTS more smashing swops, but I'm blowed if Im letting you have them, till you've shot something really worth cutting! Anyway, just in case you do.... I'm enclosing our latest "brochure". Its only a harmless hobby, you understand, no nasty money or anything like that.

        Yours, ████████████████

        CENSOR

P.S. I dont suppose theres any chance of letting me have just a couple of frames of Nana Mouskouri WITHOUT the glasses???

CENSI-SWOP ★ SERVICE ★

Send me your naughty bits and I'll send you mine!

GENUINE EXCHANGES

From "Bambi":
The Venison Kebab feast

From "Chitty Chitty Bang Bang": The Bang Bang

From "The Wizard of Oz":
The Tin Man's song: 'If only I had a ▬▬▬'

NOW Available

Also

The Cannibal Scene from "Deep Throat"

The Interesting Bit from "Death in Venice"

AND THE EVER POPULAR . . . Bit from "Mary Poppins" where Julie Andrews takes her umbrella and stuffs it up her . . . (cont.) I am under 18 ☐ (Tick)

Frankly, Graeme was not happy. "The Myxomatosis scene from Thumper, indeed!". The aesthetic integrity of the whole movie was threatened. The Arctic Tern had been an exquisitely sublime symbol of spiritual exhilaration, which in no way could be adequately conveyed by a festering rabbit. Neither would the shimmering Bertolucci-like tranquility of the 'Abbey scene' be improved by two minutes of Ali Macgraw blowing off!

Furthermore, Graeme had just completed editing the second reel, the chief feature of which was a half hour, soft-focus, slow-motion, through-the-grass-against-the-sun sequence of . . . Nana Mouskouri *without the glasses!* (She'd agreed to a 'stand-in' for

Graeme after he'd walked out on himself.) There was no way the Censor wouldn't nick the lot! But time was running short – and so was our Film – and there was little else we could do but send off the Historic 'Nude-faced Nana' reel immediately, and pray to God we got a few decent swaps in exchange. Some hopes! By return Dromedary we received:

The Three-second 'Funny sequence' from *Confessions of a Window Cleaner*.

The Abortion scene from an unreleased 'Shirley Temple'.

And the 'Ever-popular bit from Mary Poppins, where Julie Andrews takes her umberella and stuffs it up . . . the chimney!' Big flippin' deal!

CHAPTER FIFTEEN
TO THE RESCUE...

Day 49: Special emergency meeting of The Goodies Film committee.

Bill Oddie was in the chair; Graeme Garden was in a nice tweed skirt; and Tim Brooke Taylor was in tears. The Committee met, and had a long honest look at what they'd got so far.

'It emerged that we had shot about two hours of footage, which, after appropriate editing, would come down to say, roughly, twenty five minutes; give or take half an hour either way. It was unanimously agreed that it displayed, in varying degrees, complete lack of continuity; overall lousy acting, uniformly dodgy shooting, and was undeniably totally incomprehensible. One thing was clear – we had made *an Art movie!* But was it what we wanted?'

In the words of Baden Powell: "Stuff the Art – where's the ackers?" Extract from *Making Films for Pleasure and Profit.*

'We were certain of a good review in *Time Out,* and possibly a run at *The Other Cinema,* but we certainly had *not* got a Box-office-boffo-smasheroo.

It was, however, agreed that it was not 'our fault'. We had had 'jolly bad luck'. So who's fault was it? To quote B–P again;

"When in doubt . . . blame the writer."

There was one day's shooting left in which to transform a load of arty farty old codswallop into a sure-fire commercial hit. Graeme's computer had written the rotten thing – so Graeme's computer could jolly well rescue it. It was immediately shown the film, and asked some very searching questions . . .

Q *What do you think of it so far?*

A——— RUGGISH!

Q *Where did we go wrong?*

A——— GETTING A BLEEDIN'COMPUTER TO WRITE THE SCRIPT,FOR A KICK OFF.

Q *We've one day left. Is it too late?*

A——— 'COURSE NOT.KEEP FIRING THE QUESTIONS, SUNSHINE.

Q *Do you think any of it is worth keeping?*

A————— SURE.I LOVE THE TWITCHING BUNNY.THE SHIRLEY TEMPLE ABORTION IS A MIND BLOWER.JULIE ANDREWS- KNOCK OUT! ALI'S FARTING- TERRIFIC!LOTS OF GOOD STUFF.BUILD ON IT.

Q *What about the Dromedary?*

A————— GREAT LITTLE MOVER,BUT YOU SHOULD NEVER LET IT SPEAK.SOUNDS LIKE FIFTEEN GUYS IN A SKIN.SUGGEST:GET LASSIE IN TO DUB ON THE VOICE.

Q *How do we get over the bad continuity? The weather isn't the same in two shots running!*

A————— KNOCK OFF LOTS OF ''CUT-AWAYS''.SUGGEST: CLOUDS ACROSS THE SUN: SUN ACROSS THE CLOUDS:BERT FOORD:FIRE BRIGADE:AND NEWSPAPER HOARDINGS ''YUGOSLAVIAN ARMY CAUGHT IN FREAK STORM' 'ETC ETC.
WHEN IN DOUBT STICK IN QUICK SHOT OF CALENDAR PAGES TURNING, OR TRAIN WHEELS.ALSO SUGGEST:GET CHARLES BRONSON: KNOCK OFF REACTION SHOTS AND SHOVE 'EM IN WHEREVER.
ALSO SUGGEST:''QUADROPHONIC DISTRACTION''SOUND.
YOU HAVE SPEAKERS BEHIND THE AUDIENCE-RIGHT?

Q *Right...so?*

A————— SO...LIKE, YOU KNOW THE BIT WHERE YOU'VE HAD TO LOSE THE ''BIN-LESS NANA'' SCENES?

Q *Yes...*

A————— SO NOW THERE'S A NASTY CUT FROM THE ATHENIANS SCORING A TRY, STRAIGHT TO THE SHARK FIGHT,WHICH DOESN'T MAKE A LOT OF SENSE'

Q *You can say that again.*

A————— WHICH DOESN'T MAKE A LOT OF SENSE.WELL,AS SOON AS THEY'VE KICKED THE CONVERSION. ''AAAAAAAAAARGH''........
THERE'S A BLOOD-CURDLING SCREAM FROM THE BACK SPEAKERS.THE WHOLE AUDIENCE TURNS ROUND.BY THE TIME THEY'VE TURNED BACK WE'RE HALF WAY THROUGH THE SHARK FIGHT.THEY ALL THINK THEY'VE MISSED SOMETHING INCREDIBLE!MIGHT EVEN COME BACK AND SEE THE WHOLE MOVIE AGAIN.CLEVER EH?

Q *Clever. Any other little things?*

A————— YES- JON WAYNE AND BERT LANCASTER.GET THEM BACK.GREAT LITTLE TROOPERS. OH,AND A CHILD STAR....YOU MUST HAVE A CHILD STAR... ...THE NEWEST AND GREATEST.....ESSENTIAL.

Q *We'll try. You've been a whole heap of help. Thanks a lot.*

A————— DON'T MENTION IT.OH BY THE WAY,WATCH OUT FOR A TALL DARK STRANGE

And so with hope in their hearts they came to ...

CHAPTER SIXTEEN
THE FINAL DAY

And about ****ing time too. *Lord Baden-Powell*

A RACE AGAINST TIME...   SCHEDULE FOR LAST DAY'S SHOOTING

<u>6.30 AM</u>
Milkman to deliver three extra pints and
a bone.

<u>7.00 AM</u>
Exercise Lassie, and make sure she
"goes" before dubbing session. Lassie to dub
for Bonzo the Wonder Dromedary.
Will require cue cards...

<u>Also 7.00 AM</u>
Pick up Jon Wayne and Bert Lancaster.
Don't drop them. Carry to Wardrobe to
be fitted for new roles (to be decided
by Bill).

<u>Also 7.00 AM</u>
Mrs B White to temporary Maternity Ward
(Wick St Laurence R.F.C. Gents Loo).
Corporal Skratćanić to report in Midwifes
gear. Saline drip, rubber gloves, lots
of hot water, pliers etc etc. Commence
induction of Heinz. Tick Second Team
Forwards to assist.

<u>7.30 AM</u>
Camera to Weston Super Mare Grand Central
Station to shoot train wheels for
"cut-aways".
Shots 2 8 16 37 57 89 134 245 257 289
      356 456 458 460 538 544 569 600
      and 621
<u>NB</u> shoot train backing 'cos wheels
always look as if they're going backwards
on film - so this way they'll look as if
they're going forwards won't they?

<u>7.50 AM</u>
Calendar "cut-aways"...
Shots 3 9 17 38 58 90 135 146 257 200
      356 457 461 539 545 601
      and 621 (alternative)

<u>8.00 AM</u>
Camera to return to location to shoot
Charles Bronson reaction shots.
Shots 32 42 52 62 72 82 92 103
      4 5 6 and 7 201 301 406
      and 621 (alternative)

The *Charles Bronson* polyfoto *Range of Expression*

1) Anger.

2) Brooding Menace.

3) Pain.

4) Elation.

5) Gaiety.

6) Horror.

7) Coy.

8) Suffering.

9) Despair.

10) In lighter mood.

11) Understanding.

12) Dead.

13) Comic !

14) POW !

15) Song and Dance Man ! !

9.00 AM
Shoot: sun against clouds... or cloud against sun (depending on weather)
Shots 4 10 18 39 59 91 136 etc etc...
        and 621 (alternative)

<u>9.15 AM</u>
Yugoslavian Army to report (except for Corp. Skratćanić) in tin-foil bras and transparent pantaloons etc. Please blanco trusses. Final rehearsal of "Dance of the Seven Surgical Appliances"

<u>9.20 AM</u>
"Heinz" to be "delivered". More hot water. Corp. Skratćanić to change out of Midwife gear, and join Dance Rehearsal.

Bill Oddie recalls the final day:

All in all we had one hundred and thirty four shots to do on that last day. Through-out the filming so far, our average had been just under four and a half shots per day. Clearly we were going to have to put on a bit of a spurt. By nine fifteen, the whole location was a hive of industrious activity. No sooner did problems occur, than they were faced and defeated. Charles Bronson's uncontrollable childish giggling was stifled by showing him clips of his latest movie, and within half an hour, we had captured the full gamut of his single expression. The cupidity of nature had provided us with a flat grey day . . . no sun, and no clouds! But a passable simulation was rapidly achieved by dangling an incandescent Wot-Wig from an invisible thread, and blowing cigarette smoke across it. So we got our cut-aways.

Anyone passing the 'Maternity Ward' could hardly have failed to be uplifted by the strenuous roars of "Heave" from Scratcanic and the Wick St Laurence Second-team forwards, which testified to their scrummaging efforts in the tenacious crotch of Mrs B White, as they attempted to extract the reluctant Heinz.

Throughout the unit, the adrenaline flowed like sweat, as shot after shot was stuffed 'into the can'. At last, we were winning! Surely nothing could stop us now?

Suddenly . . . the sound of Lassie's heart-rending whimpering was drowned by an ominous rumble; and a shadow like a vaste gloomy vulture of doom fell across the location. Concorde – no less – and it was coming in to land – slap bang in the middle of the Wick St Lawrence Second Team pitch. As it delved its way to a halt, scything through the caravans, its Marlin-snout neatly kebabbing the Athenians – we noted, with dismay, the insignia emblazoned on its hulk

It was the private plane of the Shah of Rhaine! The door opened, and out curled a glistening red carpet. It looked like a red carpet, but it was in fact the slavering tongue of Sir Louis Bunce. Down it slithered The Shah-ess, Her Almightiness Mrs Edna Tole (former President of Venezuela) and finally himself, The Shah of Rhain (silly joke, and chief investor in The Goodies Film). He had arrived, no doubt, to exercise the backer's inexorable right to screw everything up at the last minute. Nervously, we recalled the computer's final warning: "Beware a tall dark stranger!". Horrifically, we remembered the Shah's conditions for letting us spend his ill-earned loot:

'THE FILM MUST FEATURE RITA ACAPULCO. NO CAMEL JOKES AND NO BELLY DANCERS!'

He came straight to the point:

"Rita's knockers!" demanded the Shah. "I have come to see film of Rita's knockers. This is the twelfth movie I have visited today. I have invested in them all. They will *all* be box office boffo smasheroos, because they ALL feature Rita's knockers. The public can't get enough of Rita's knockers . . . and neither can I. I wish to see them. Now. Arrange a viewing!"

'Mr Tact' leapt forward, with a piece of utterly imprudent information: "They've been cut!"

"Off?" The Shah went white (well, beige anyway)

"No, not *off*. Out. The knockers are out. Not that they were ever in, you see, we . . ." The Shah glowered: "There will be knockers in this film . . . or I raise the price of petrol!"

In his agitation he shifted his balance, allowing Sir Bunce to retrieve his tongue: "Fear not me old Shah. We shall reinstate the knockers. The knockers will be instantly re-cast. The knockers will be featured more conspicuously than ever. They will be unavoidably blatant. Rita Acapulco's knockers shall play . . . the camel's humps!"

The crowd gasped. The Shah hissed "Camel! *What camel?????!?*"

The untimely clatter of approaching hooves was almost drowned by the frantic protestations of 'Mr Tact'.

"There isn't a camel. There's only a dog. Well, when I say a dog . . . I must admit . . . it doesn't look *much* like a dog . . . it looks more like, well . . . a camel . . ."

"First camel joke! £2 a gallon!" ordered the Shah.

"But its not a camel . . . 'cos its a dromedary. 'Cos – as every schoolboy knows – and as every Shah knows, I'm sure – a camel has *two* humps, whilst a dromedary has only *one* hump, and what we have here is clearly ∴ .." Tim's thesis was rudely undermined by the perky arrival of Bonzo the Wonder Dromedary, now rendered all the more wonderful, by the fact that it now undeniably sported – two humps!

The Shah was not unobservant "Two Humps! Its a Camel Joke! £5 a gallon!"

"It never used to have two humps" pleaded Tim meekly.

"£10 a gallon!"

Graeme, in whom guilt is often the mother of invention, seemed, as medical adviser, to be best qualified to explain the metamorphosis: "It is definitely *not* a camel. It has only got *one* hump. It IS definitely, therefore, a dromedary. It is, however, I admit, a dromedary . . . with a very large boil!"

"In that case" announced the Shah, compassionately drawing his scimitar, "I shall lance it"!

And so saying, he plunged his blade into the rear hump. Out burst . . . Jon Wayne! Clutching his miniscule botty, the punctured midget let out a yell so shocking that Mrs B White leapt two feet in the air and instantly gave birth. Heinz, the newest and greatest child star shot out like a ball from the scrum.

The Yugoslavian Army, till now models of military impassivity in their diaphonous trousers and tin-foil bras, laughed so convulsively that every truss and appliance sprang asunder for the last time releasing folds of fat that palpitated with uncontrollable mirth, like a thousand juddering jellies.

"BELLY DANCERS!" screamed the Shah!

With a sweep of his scimitar he cut off diplomatic relations . . . and ordered the immediate invasion of the West Country!

RHAINIAN FORCES ON THE MOVE

THE **Sun**

RRA-VO! 6p

From our War Correspondent.

The full-scale invasion of Wick St. Lawrence, Weston-super-Mare and surrounding countryside seemed to be imminent last night. The Shah of Rhaine announced that owing to the unpardonable in- sults perpetrated on the...

Nun but the brave!

everley Hills and Rita Acapulco

lovely Miss Acapulco, re- tinned to be the Cinebe-

fore Productions spe- tacular

THE GUARDIAN

Somerset under seige

PLE ORDERS VENEZUELAN PPORT . . .

A diplomat source revealed today that the unprecedented provocation leading to the invasion, by air and sea, of the county of Somers...

made the following statement "Never in the field of movie makin...

the continuing bombard- ent of camel jokes and out- ageous harem stories, not to mention lewd suggestions as to the effect of belly dancing the eyesight of the ...ik, had made dip- totally unten- political

average
lomatic relations totally u
able within the current p
climate.

His country had no
therefore, but to orde
scale denudation and
tion of the whole
rounding the sourc
insidious proclamat

INVASION

DIFF UFF WICK
ck St. Lawrence 15 pts.
ardiff over 90's 30 pts.

This memorable g
played under som
difficult circumstan
mainly to the ine
the local Fir
failing to p
of burn
Wick's
was
on

by our roving reporter Lobby Lud

Holiday-makers, enjoy- ing the recent spell of hot weather in Somer- set, were surprised to find themselves being strafed by jet fighters as they sunned themselve on the b...

DAILY Mirror
BRITAIN'S BIGGEST DAILY SALE 7p

"Keep 'em rolling . . ."
Lord Baden-Powell

An extract from Making Films for Pleasure and Profit by Lord Baden-Powell

GRAEME GARDEN
ON THE WESTON FRONT
FILMED AS IT ACTUALLY HAPPENED!
AA
RAC
STARRING
JACK NICHOLSON · JAMES CAAN ·
CHARLES BRONSON · MRS B.WHITE ·
DONALD SUTHERLAND · ELLIOT DUCK ·
MICHAEL YORK · LORD LUCAN ·
ROGER MOORE · PAUL NEWMAN ·
ROBERT REDFORD · STEVE McQUEEN ·
NANA MOUSKOURI · BOLSHOI BALLET ·
OLIVER REED · KEITH KONG ·
JON WAYNE · BERT LANCASTER ·
YUGOSLAVIAN ARMY ·
AND INTRODUCING
BEVERLEY HILLS
AND/OR
RITA ACAPULCO
AND MANY MANY MORE!!!

No, not a lovely bore

This has been a heavy week for the film reviewer. A new Fellini: 'Snow White and the Seven Thousand Dwarfs' (more of which next week) and several films, inevitably I suppose, attempting to cash in on the recent raid on Weston Super Mare: "Victory at Weston", "Raid on Weston" and "Operation Robert Bolt". But none of these can compare with the definitive Ken Russell version "All Quiet on the Weston Front". (All cinemas in the World, this week).

"All Quiet" is a triumph. Russell has made a masterpiece that will surely stand side by side with da Vinci's Mona Lisa, for centuries to come. Every shot has a purpose, not just to tell the story, but to create a texture that builds up into a tapestry which defies its description as a mere 'film'. From the crash of the first milk bottle to the last exploding nun the symbolism is obvious. The cleverly out-of-focus Arctic Tern brilliantly intercut with the birth of a child (played here by newcomer, Heinz, a name I'm sure we'll be seeing on posters for years to come) succeeds during these few seconds in explaining Man's purpose here on earth where, for the last few thousand years, all the religions in the World have failed.

The story itself is almost unimportant, and it is not my place to tell it here. The Sheikhdom of Rainnh and all fellow OPEC countries are on a war footing. The Shah together with his Generals Charles Bronson, Rod McKuen and Sheikh Ahleg, agonise over the decision whether or not to send in their forces. Russell here uses the device of a film within a film to describe the inner struggles of these lonely men. The quick cuts from the impassive face of Charles Bronson to Thumper with myxamatosis, Shirley Temple in an unusual pose and Ali McGraw giving a whole new meaning to the phrase "Love is not having to say you're sorry", is a short moment of confusion. But this, as we soon see, is intentional. From the very moment that Mary Poppins' umbrella hits the chimney the planes are in the air and 'Operation Robert Bolt' is on.

Meanwhile in Wick St Lawrence a strange army is being mobilised. Graeme Garden has taken overall control (A superb performance here from Graeme Garden and Nana Mouskouri). His forces are limited but well deployed. A padded cell, clearly marked 'Welcome to Britain' is moved to Sand Bay. While at Weston Bay a shark (Bill Oddie) is being released into the water. Secrecy is the keynote and the several hundred belly dancers who are painting the runways of Weston Super Mare Airport bright green are not to know that their seemingly useless labours are a vital part of Graeme's overall plan. Likewise Tim Brooke-Taylor (a beautifully observed portrayal here, by Tim Brooke-Taylor, of a bitchy, waspish failure who resents being told what to do) was reluctantly leading 600 more belly dancers to the foot of Bleadon Hill.

In Wick St Lawrence itself, as a cloud clears the sun, 5000 drivers are driving their cars into a circle. Women, children and Tim's hat are to be defended to the last chauffeur. 15,000 belly dancers are being made-up as the camp echoes to the elastic twangs of an army preparing for battle. Suddenly the air is rent with the scream of an able-seaman cracking under pressure (Bryan Forbes) but the danger of mass panic is quickly averted by a crunching tackle from the Wick St Lawrence Fly Half (The Wick St Lawrence Fly Half). As the shadows of the goal posts lengthen the army is ready. Now all it can do is wait.

Thirty thousand feet above their heads a converted Boeing 707 is acting as the operations room for the Rhainnian and Allied forces. Charles Bronson raises an eyebrow and on this word of command the signal is sent out. Just off the coast of Weston Super Mare 1500 radios crackle into life "Eyebrow Raised" "Eyebrow Raised". Fifteen hundred disguised fishing vessels divide into two parties and head for Weston and Sand Bays. So far Graeme had been right.

Five Hercules bombers on a routine flight over France change course. The Eyebrow had been raised. Weston Super Mare was to be the new destination. There was no turning back.

At this point I would question Russell's inclusion of a genuinely funny moment from "The Confessions of a Window Cleaner", however subliminal, but my feeling of shock and surprise was nothing to the look of horror on the faces of the Arab landing party on Sand Bay. The sight of the shark rearing up before them was bad enough. But a singing shark:

"Yum yum
Sheikh Yerbum"

this was more than they could take and to a man they fled back out to sea. Four hundred were killed in this retreat and fifteen hundred badly injured. But not one of these men, had they known, would have swapped places with their comrades on Weston Bay.

It is not the duty of a film critic to give all the details of a story, indeed this can be very irritating for the reader who may actually wish to see the film.

However Weston Bay was the scene of true devastation. As we follow the advance party, we see it through the eyes of the Arabs themselves (The Rhainnian War Records Film Unit are credited with 'Additional photography'). Confronted with a large container 'Welcome to Britain' they suspect a trap and blast it to pieces. As the smoke clears an apparition can gradually be made out. Like a Phoenix rising from the ashes it staggers towards the soldiers, it's contorted features giving them the impression of a half crazed creature. They are wrong. It is a completely crazed creature (Keith Moon). Here Russell provides a twist to the King Kong story by making his monster entirely unsympathetic. When the injured Loon is finally overcome by the few remaining survivors, hardened press men at the preview I attended broke into cheers rising to a cataclysmic roar as the final drumstick is rammed home.

News of the setbacks reach the Boeing still circling thousands of feet above. Bronson raises another eyebrow (the visual effects are brilliant throughout the film) and the message instantly crackles through to the pilots of the five Hercules. "The Second Eyebrow is raised". Things must be going wrong. The contingency plan must be put into operation. They must land at Weston Super Mare Airport. The navigators are confused; thousands of naked nuns swim before their eyes. The Airport has vanished. A rear gunner reports unusual strips of bright green – paddy fields perhaps? In the body of the plane the Arab troops are tense. The 'double' milkman, his face painted white, sits in his reconstructed milk float. He shifts uneasily from red top to gold top to frozen chickens. A cry goes up, "Ahead sir, the Landing Lights!"

On the ground below Tim has heard the sound of the planes' engines overhead and makes a final check that all his belly-dancers are in position. Forty yards apart, in parallel formation, their glistening orange hair-pieces (Wotwigs) point the way to Bleadon Hill. Five Hercules Bombers hurtle down between them and crash spectacularly against the side of the hill. (At least I presume it was spectacular as your reviewer unfortunately missed the incident for just at that moment an ear-splitting scream, thanks to the excellent quadrophonic sound system, appeared to come from the back of the cinema and I had turned my head. I must certainly go and see this film again).

Meanwhile at Wick St Lawrence Graeme is quelling the premature celebrations. They are still heavily out-numbered by Arab survivors. The war is not yet won and the final battle is still to be fought.

At Bleadon the Bleadon vicar's wife soon cracks under pressure (an unnecessarily bloody scene I thought). The re-organised invaders from sea and air now know their target – the Wick St Lawrence Rugby Ground. The more superstitious amongst them, all of them, are wary. Could this be Wick St Lawrence of Arabia? A Shihtzu leaves the vicarage unnoticed and heads North.

The climax of the film should not be given away. Go and see it for yoursrself.

What happens is this.

The thin green line of

chauffeurs finally gives. They have defended manfully. Not a jack nor a crank handle has missed its mark – but they are beaten. The next attack would be conclusive. The enemy have held back, wary of the enormous mortar, cleverly disguised as a camera lens yet strangely silent. The Arabs had waited as they had watched it being taken to pieces and re-assembled in a matter of seconds. But they would wait no longer. The advance is ordered. No-one will be spared; not the women, not the children, not even the hat!

But the gallant defenders of Wick St Lawrence are not going to give way easily. Graeme turns to his black Yugoslavian belly dancers and gives the order to fire. He claps his hands to his ears as an almighty TWANG announces that 25,000 trusses have successfully released their missiles. To the Arabs the sky is momentarily dark with falling poodles, 25,000 of them, but apart from a few nasty nips they are undismayed. A loose scrum crashes through their ranks causing untold damage – but still the advance moves on. Yet they are soon to pause, confronted by two nuns and a shaggy creature (Ken Russell himself). Were these black and white creatures giant penguins? Was that a polar bear? Where were they? The Antarctic?

Using this lull Graeme plays his last card. Quickly he saddles his mount, leaps on and gallops into the middle of the Rugby pitch. His gallant steed rears up on its four hind legs and lets out a mighty "Woof". "Hail Graeme our mighty leader". "Hail Bonzo the Wonder Dog".

The otherwise admirable sub-titles become unclear at this point of the film: "This camel is a six legged dromedary and it barks". "You are right Ahmed, perhaps it would be wiser to return to our native lands." "Do you have a good analyst?" "Indeed I used to think so".

But Russell's modern parable suddenly becomes clear. It begins to rain and out of the clouds comes a shining white plane. "Is it a bird? Is it a plane? No it's Henry Kissinger come to play the part of Bill."

The film ends with a joyous celebration. Henry Kissinger, within minutes has made peace.

Both armies are to *share* the Hat. As the camera pans back on this feastive scene the two orators are in full flight (Beverly Hills and Rita Acapulco excellently dubbed by Laurence Olivier and Orson Welles). Yugoslavs and Arabs join hands and dance to the music (The Athenians) as they swig the milk (The Milk Marketing Board) and feast themselves on poodles' eyes (Fanny Craddock).

Ken Russell has not just made a film. He has made history. At last here is a carefully made, well thought out film. Do go and see it.

THE ST

scouts and scouting

GREY WOLF'S JOTTINGS
The fiftieth anniversary of Lt Col 'Podge' Bulstrode's gallant yet fatal attempt to teach lions to tie knots is being celebrated by scouts all over the World this week by hundreds of woggle twirling competitions.

The jungle drums also tell me that a new revised edition of Lord B-P's "Making Films for Please and Profit" was published last Friday. This authoritative work has probably been the single most important factor responsible for the state of the present British Film Industry. Nowhere can this be better seen than in ex-cub Ken Russell's latest film "All Quiet on the Weston Front". It's a ripping yarn and well worth a trek. One word of warning though, all the hair is a bit long and much of it a strange ginger colour.

Five pence a job week will soon be with us and I'm offering special prizes for the best suggestions on helping old ladies across motorways.

THE TIMES

Plus FREE Speaker worth £2.95 and FREE Aerial worth £2.95
Our Price £50.95

But suddenly the Combine Harvester stopped; and with one bound Ivan was free.

THE END

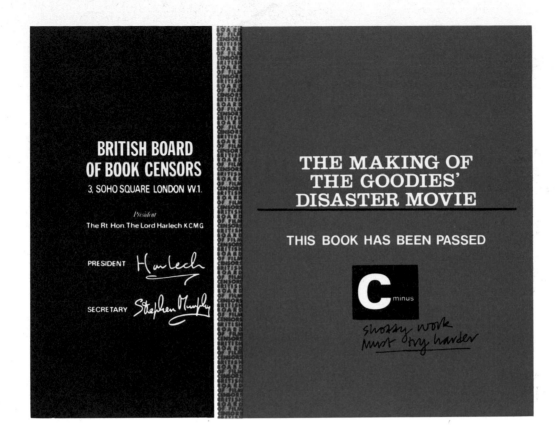

BRITISH BOARD
OF BOOK CENSORS

3, SOHO SQUARE LONDON W.1.

President
The Rt Hon. The Lord Harlech K C M G

PRESIDENT *Harlech*

SECRETARY *Stephen Murphy*

THE MAKING OF
THE GOODIES'
DISASTER MOVIE

THIS BOOK HAS BEEN PASSED

C minus

*shoddy work
must try harder*

THE GOODIES FILE

A MESSAGE FROM THE PUBLISHERS

We believe that this is an important book. The documents which go to make up THE GOODIES FILE were brought to us by Mrs. Edna Tole, one-time employee of the men in question, and now seeking to reveal to the world the activities of the growing band of secret figures who even now move among us, operating "without the law".

On reading the file, you may find it boring. More to the point, it *is* boring. Nevertheless, we felt that it was our duty to assist Mrs. Tole in her ambition - to expose the facts, and make a million pounds.

But the last word must go to Mrs. Edna Tole, who gave her reasons for this exposé as: "... at least a million pounds, but also to show the world that the so-called 'Goodies' (Goodies? Baddies more like) are no more than a bunch of lying, thieving, swivel-eyed, two-faced, lousy sons of ..." Well, it's impossible to describe - read it instead.

0 7221 1881 3   HUMOUR   £2.25

Not to be read by:
Tim Brooke-Taylor
Bill Oddie
Graeme Garden

AND IF YOUR SANITY SURVIVES .....

You'll love reading the sensational account of the Goodies' futile attempt to defend their good name. THE GOODIES' BOOK OF CRIMINAL RECORDS is all you ever wanted to know about the terrible trio. And we really do mean *all* ...

0 7221 3960 8   HUMOUR   £2.25